Chinese Wus

Taiji Quan —Yang-Style

Yu Gongbao

FOREIGN LANGUAGES PRESS   BEIJING

First Edition   1996
Second Printing   1998

ISBN 7-119-01807-8

© Foreign Languages Press, Beijing, China, 1996

Published by Foreign Languages Press
24 Baiwanzhuang Road, Beijing 100037, China

Distributed by China International Book Trading Corporation
35 Chegongzhuang Xilu, Beijing 100044, China
P.O. Box 399, Beijing, China

Printed in the People's Republic of China

CONTENTS

I *Taiji* and *Taiji Quan*

Born on the soil of ancient Chinese culture, the Chinese Wushu absorbs the flavour of Chinese classical philosophy.

To use parts of the human body as symbols and to express the knowledge of life and the world through the combination of movements of these symbols are the important intentions of Chinese Wushu. In this sense, Wushu was one of the ways used by the Chinese people in ancient times to interpret the world outlook.

It took a long time to forge the link between Wushu and philosophy. Wushu in early times was nothing more than combinations of simple movements of combat; it, therefore, had primitive practical use. War led to the trememdous growth of Wushu, adding the characters of offence and defence. Outstanding strategists in ancient times attached great importance to Wushu, injecting strategic ideas into its theory and principles. That represented an important philosophical revolution in Wushu. The wide use of Wushu among the common people as a technique for self-defence gave individualistic character to the sport; it helped to diversify Chinese boxing with or without equipment and the formation of the different schools. All this served to lay the foundation for inclusion of Chinese classical philosophy into the boxing. As a result of the progress and development of the society, Wushu was used for multiple purposes, including life enhancement, entertainment and show. The participation of many scholars brought Wushu a rich cultural character. This marked the beginning of the stage in which Wushu and philosophy were consciously combined. By the time of the Ming and Qing dynasties, the systems of the main boxing schools of Wushu were basically formed, and most of them contained the heavy flavour of philosophy. *Taiji Quan* was the most representative of all schools of Wushu.

Taiji Quan is also called "philosophical boxing," meaning that its principles and techniques all contain the idea of *Taiji* in Chinese classical philosophy. To learn *Taiji Quan* calls, first of all, for understanding this philosophical thought. This helps to know the techniques of *Taiji Quan*.

The idea of *Taiji* is, in fact, a systematic thought of balance.

Taiji refers to a primitive state in Chinese philosophy. It is a natural existence. The life of man was a state of *Taiji* in the earliest stage, just like the baby in the body of a mother. Lao Zi, the representative of Taoism, spoke very highly of this state when he wrote that people formed much tension in their daily lives which led to illnesses. Therefore, people should relax their bodies and minds through exercise to return to the infant state.

Chinese classical philosophy holds that all things are born of *Taiji*. The whole process is stated in detail in the *Book of Changes* written in the Zhou Dynasty (1100-221 B.C.): "*Taiji* causes the two opposites, the two opposites cause the four seasons, and the four seasons cause the eight natural phenomena (denoting heaven, earth, thunder, wind, water, fire, mountains and lakes)." The eight phenomena cause all things. The two opposites mentioned here are the yin (negative) and yang (positive), which exist in all system. The picture (Fig. 1-1) shows the famous "*Taiji* Chart," in which the black represents yin and the white yang. They are supplementary to each other, transform themselves into each other and depend on each other. The harmony and balance

Fig. 1-1

between yin and yang constitute the "*Taiji* state." The human body is also composed of yin and yang. When yin and yang are balanced, both the body and mind are in a good state; however, their imbalance leads to illness. Therefore, to improve the physical qualities and prevent illness begins with the adjustment of yin and yang. Offence and defence also form a contradiction of yin and yang; if the relationship between offence and defence is handled well, the key point of combat is grasped. Therefore, to grasp the rules of the changes between yin and yang of the human body is an important way to improve the ability of combat. The ideas described above form the basic train of thought for *Taiji Quan*.

The *Taiji* philosophical thought is embodied in the play of every exercise of the *Taiji Quan*.

Yin and yang are divided in every movement: the relationship of yin and yang is involved in every motion of the *Taiji Quan*, whether in a fixed form or in a process.

There is a clear distinction between the empty and the solid, and between the above and the below in every movement. In the Single Whip exercise (Fig. 1-2), the left hand in front is the open palm and belongs to yang, and the right hand in the rear is the hook and belongs to yin. When the head is up slightly, it is yang, and when the crotch is relaxed and down, it is yin. When the weight is on the left leg, it is solid and belongs to yang; then the right leg is empty and belongs to yin. At the same time, every yin and yang element implies the tendency to transform itself into the opposite. This is why the play of the *Taiji Quan* changes constantly and continuously like the moving clouds and flowing water.

There are curves everywhere: The *Taiji* Chart is round in shape. Between yin and yang are harmonious coexistence and soft transformation. The curved movements conform best to the natural state of the structure of the human body, making it easy to transform and adjust the yin and yang relationship smoothly (Fig. 1-3).

Fig. 1-2

Fig. 1-3

Motion and stillness exist together. The movements of the *Taiji Quan* are relaxed and slow. They call for stillness in motion to achieve the relaxation of the mind and body. At the same time, while in the fixed form, there must be motion in stillness so that the movements do not discontinue and the mind and energy flow do not stop. Motion and stillness are the two opposites of a contradiction—the yin and yang. The coexistence of motion and stillness is the embodiment of the *Taiji Quan* idea: "There is yin in yang, and yang in yin."

Hardness and softness are combined: if too hard, it is easy to break; if too soft, it is easy to damage. The *Taiji Quan* stresses softness to achieve hardness. In the light and soft movements is an imposing manner, assisted by the mind at the same time. Where there is the body form, there is the mind. What is tempered is the changeable and flexible "hardness." While executing the movements, softness is implied while hardness is shown in form. So exists the integral whole, whether in advance or retreat, in rise or fall, or in closing or opening. When one part moves, all parts of the body move. This effectively helps to temper the integrity and harmony of the human body and increase the harmony between yin and yang.

The *Taiji* thought is a strict system and it is embodied in the *Taiji Quan* in many ways. I have given only a few examples to illustrate the points. The readers have to carefully understand the more profound intentions of the *Taiji Quan* through their own practice.

II Origin

The Yang-style *Taiji Quan* is one of the important schools of the Chinese *Taiji Quan*. Since its birth, it has spread rapidly and won wide popularity among the people. In recent years, the Yang-style *Taiji Quan* has also become popular in other countries and is now one of the most influential schools of the Chinese Wushu.

The Yang-style *Taiji Quan* was born in the Qing Dynasty (1644-1911). Its originator was Yang Luchan. He and his later generations made outstanding contributions to the spread and development of this boxing style. Hence the Yang-style *Taiji Quan*. The original name of Yang Luchan was Yang Fukui. He was born in a peasant family in Yongnian County, Hebei Province, in the reign of Emperor Daoguang (1821-1850). He took to martial arts as a child and practised *Erlang Quan* in his village. Later, he followed the *Taiji Quan* master Chen Changxing in Chenjiagou in Wenxian County, Henan Province, from whom he learned boxing.

There are many other prevailing stories about how Yang Luchan learned his skills. The most popular is that he was an apprentice in the Taihetang Drugstore in Yongnian County, the manager of which was Chen Dehu from Chenjiagou, Wenxian County, Henan Province. One day, some hooligans came to the drugstore to make trouble, forcing Chen Dehu to use his *Taiji* skills to deal with them. Yang Luchan saw this and was quite happy. He repeatedly begged Chen to teach him his skills. Chen refused at first, but was later so moved by Yang's sincerity that he recommended that he could become proficient in

Chenjiagou Village, where Chen Changxing was the best boxing master. From then on, Yang Luchan began to learn *Taiji Quan* under Chen's personal coaching. He practised very hard for 18 years and finally learned its real essence.

Another story tells about Yang Luchan going by himself to Chenjiagou, where his request was refused. However, he stayed in the village by working for a local family. Every evening, he watched from afar as Chen Changxing taught his students; then he secretly practised when he returned. He persisted for years and gained a rudimentary understanding. One day when he was practising *Taiji Quan* by himself, Chen Changxing saw him and was impressed by his hard work. He finally agreed to accept him as an apprentice and teach him the real skills. This was the popular story of "stealing boxing skills" heard among the Chinese Wushu circles.

Before Yang Luchan learned *Taiji Quan* from Chen Changxing, *Taiji Quan* had been popular for many years. However, there is still no fixed conclusion about the origin of *Taiji Quan*. According to historical data, something like *Taiji Quan* already existed in the Han Dynasty (206 B.C.-220) and the Tang Dynasty (618-907). The theory of yin and yang, which is the theoretical basis for *Taiji Quan*, was already systematized in the period of the Warring States (475-221 B.C.) and was applied in various fields, such as the agricultural calendar, astronomical research and medicine. *The Yellow Emperor's Canon of Medicine*, an important ancient medical classical book, analyzed the human body with the help of the yin and yang theory, setting a precedent for its application to life enhancement. This was very important to the later formation of the *Taiji Quan* system.

In the Han Dynasty, the Daoyin exercise became very popular. People coupled the movements of the limbs with

7

breathing to change the human body into different forms in order to invigorate blood circulation and energy flow and improve functions of the internal organs. The movements in Daoyin exercise are graceful and varied in forms. Implying the meaning of opening, closing, empty and solid, they became the technical start of the *Taiji Quan* and Qigong routines. From the Daoyin pictures found in the Han tombs unearthed at Mawangdui in Changsha, Hunan Province, in 1973, we arrived at this conclusion. The pictures were verified as relics of the Western Han Period. As shown in the pictures, the Daoyin movements are lively, and some of them have certain similarities to the modern *Taiji Quan* (Figs. 2-1–3). By the Tang Dynasty (618-907), *Taiji Quan* had taken an embryonic form. Historical data show that Xu Xuanping, who lived in seclusion in Nanyang in Henan Province in the Tang Dynasty, played a 37-form *Taiji Gong* which looked like the continuously flowing water in the Changjiang River (Yangtze River) and therefore was also called *Chang Quan*. Many of the names of its exercises were similar to those of the *Taiji Quan* of today. Li Daozi, another man in the Tang Dynasty, also introduced a boxing similar to *Taiji Quan* in many aspects. It can be seen, therefore, that although *Taiji Quan* had not gained momentum, it had already started. By the Song Dynasty (960-1279), various kinds of *Wushu* prospered and were even used on the battlefield. Boxing schools of various styles came into being, making this period one of further progress. By the Ming Dynasty, the *Taiji Quan* system was formally established; it was further supplemented and developed during the Qing Dynasty.

Yang Luchan, having learned the essence of *Taiji Quan* from Chen Changxing, returned to his own village. Whenever he fought with anyone, he won. Because he used his magic power to overcome stronger power and his boxing movements looked very soft but could overcome hard power, his boxing was known as the *Mian Quan* or "soft boxing."

Yang Luchan was later invited to teach his boxing method in Beijing, with many princes, dukes and other nobles learning his skills. While in the capital city, he was often challenged by others and showed his superb skills, thus earning him the nickname of "Invincible Yang."

In teaching his boxing, Yang Luchan made some changes to what he had learned in order to meet the needs of boxing enthusiasts and to enable more people to grasp the essential points of *Taiji Quan*. He simplified the playing process, revised some leaping and jumping movements, and softened some of the violent power-releasing methods. His reforms changed the style of *Taiji Quan*, leading to the emergence of the influential Yang-style.

By revising the boxing frame, Yang Luchan laid the foundation for his own style. It was further perfected by following generations so that the Yang-style *Taiji Quan*

Fig. 2-1

Fig. 2-2

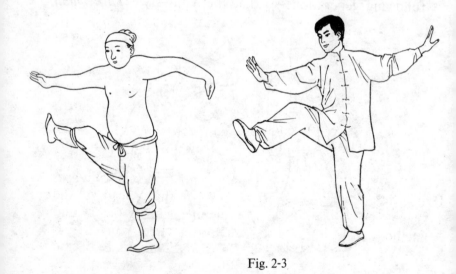

Fig. 2-3

could be carried forward. Yang Banhou (1837-1892), Lu-chan's second son, and Yang Jianhou (1839-1917), Lu-chan's third son, both learned the boxing from him, and helped him to teach. Yang Banhou was particularly good at combat skills and had a complete mastery of clever changes in the application of the different power to different movements. Yang Jianhou was good not only at boxing, but also with various weapons, including spears, rods and swords. While teaching their skills, the brothers made changes to the boxing frame to make their style even more characteristic. As their stances combined both hard and soft, upright and steady movements, the Yang-style *Taiji Quan* was particularly recommended by many in Wushu circles of the day.

Among the members of the third generation of the Yang family, it was Yang Chengfu (1883-1936), the third son of Yang Jianhou, who made great contributions to the development of *Taiji Quan*. Yang Chengfu had learned boxing skills from his father since childhood, and devoted himself to the theory and methods of *Taiji Quan*. His frame of movements is free, easy, light and soft. When in play, his movements are continuous and closely connected with a strong appeal. Yang Chengfu was invited to teach *Taiji Quan* in Beijing, Shanghai, Hangzhou and Guangzhou with disciples from all over the country. He revised the old boxing frame several times, finalizing the Yang-style *Taiji Quan* routines that have become popular among *Taiji Quan* enthusiasts.

Apart from the Yang family, many other Wushu specialists played an important role in the spread of the Yang-style *Taiji Quan* and development of its theory and methods. Among these representatives were:

Wu Yuxiang (1812-1880). He was born in the same Yongnian County in Hebei Province as Yang Luchan. As he took to Wushu, he learned *Taiji Quan* from Yang Luchan. Later, he went to Henan to learn the Chen-style *Taiji Quan*. He devoted himself to martial arts, and created the Wu Yuxiang style of *Taiji Quan* on the basis of the Yang and Chen schools. Wu Yuxiang made great contributions to the development of theory. On the basis of the book *On Taiji Quan* written by his predecessor, he wrote the *Mental Solutions to Thirteen Walking Exercises*, *Main Instructions for Push Hand* and *Ten Essential Points for Body Techniques*.

Wu Jianquan (1870-1942) of the Manchu ethnic group. His father Quan You learned the Yang-style *Taiji Quan* from Yang Luchan and Yang Banhou to be a boxing master. Wu Jianquan practised boxing skills with his father since childhood and improved the soft and round parts of Yang-style *Taiji Quan*. He also reformed some of the jumping and leaping movements to form a new school called the "Wu-style *Taiji Quan*."

Xu Yusheng (1879-1945). A Wushu enthusiast, he learned the Yang-style *Taiji Quan* from Yang Jianhou. As an official of the Ministry of Education in Beiping (now Beijing), and out of his interest in Wushu, he invited Wu Jianquan, Yang Chengfu and other boxing masters to teach the boxing in Beiping to make it more popular.

Chen Weiming (1881-1958). Born in Hubei Province, he learned the boxing from Yang Chengfu. He wrote the *Book of Taiji Quan* and *Questions and Answers on Taiji*, and founded the "Zhirou Boxing Society."

Wu Zhiqing (1887-?). He was born in Anhui Province and learned *Taiji Quan* from Yang Chengfu. He founded the "China Wushu Society" and wrote the book, *Orthodox School of Taiji*. This deals with the origin and methods of *Taiji Quan* and exerted great influence on later generations.

Fu Zhongwen (1907-?). He began to learn the Yang-style *Taiji Quan* in his childhood from Yang Chengfu. He accompanied his teacher in providing boxing lessons and lectures in different parts of the country; from this he learnt the essence of the boxing. Later, he founded the "Yongnian *Taiji Quan* Society" in Shanghai, and trained large numbers of *Taiji Quan* specialists and enthusiasts. He wrote a number of books on the theory and methods of *Taiji Quan*.

Li Yaxuan (1893-1976). A disciple of Yang Chengfu, he accumulated rich practical and teaching experience. Later, he moved to Sichuan Province to disseminate the Yang-style *Taiji Quan*. He had many disciples and apprentices with great influence in southwest China.

Zheng Manqing (1901-1975). Born in Zhejiang Province, he was frequently ill and tried to find some way to restore his health. Learning boxing from a disciple of Yang Chengfu, he not only cured his illness but became an expert at the boxing. He went to Taiwan where he disseminated the art of *Taiji Quan*. He also taught the boxing in Europe and America. Having accumulated experience and knowledge for decades, he revised and condensed the traditional Yang-style *Taiji Quan* into a 37-form exercise routine, known as the "Zheng Zi *Taiji Quan*." He also left many books on the boxing for later generations.

Dong Yingjie. Born in Hebei Province, he was a disciple of Yang Chengfu and lived with him. Having devoted decades to *Taiji Quan*, he founded his own school. His boxing movements were upright, slow, light and calm, and his play was close to perfection. He travelled with Yang Chengfu to various parts of the country to teach boxing, later teaching the art in Hong Kong, Singapore and Macao for many years with a good reputation. He also wrote

Explanations for the Taiji Quan, teaching beginners how to play the Yang-style *Taiji Quan.*

Besides those mentioned, many other *Taiji Quan* specialists and enthusiasts have made contributions to the popularization of the Yang-style *Taiji Quan.*

Although the Yang-style originated from the Chen-style, it has formed its own salient features in the course of its development. The main differences between the two schools are as follows:

1. In the boxing frame, the Chen-style *Taiji Quan* has many obvious movements which conserve power and form clear rhythms in the snapping, shaking and power-releasing movements. In the Yang-style boxing, the movements which conserve power have almost become indistinct or changed with no clear rhythm in their external forms. The limb and body turns have also become flat.

2. Chen-style boxing features many jumping starts and quick-turning movements. The execution of these movements calls for constant shifts of body weight to different legs. In the Yang-style routines, no such movements exist and the shift of body weight in all these movements is slow and even. It also calls for symmetrical changes to the left and right. There are some rise and fall movements, but these call for slow rise and fall motions and gradual transitions.

3. In the Chen-style *Taiji Quan*, the player's expression must be integrated with the boxing posture; some changes, such as stillness or motion, open or close, are possible. However, in Yang-style, the expression remains the same throughout the play of the whole exercise and coordinates with the evenness of the movements.

4. The names of some movements in both schools are the same or similar, but their external forms and

essentials have become partially or completely different. This merits special attention when one is learning. In the Single Whip, there are differences in both the direction of the limbs and the mechanical structure of the body (Fig. 2-4).

Despite all this, the Chen and Yang styles, which are the two major schools of Chinese *Taiji Quan*, conform to each other in theory and principles. For example, the main stress is put on the softness of the movements. The softness is tempered to become hardness, and importance is attached to the training of internal thinking. The boxing frame is used to channel the internal energy and breathing.

While the peculiar features of the Yang-style *Taiji Quan* was taking shape, the technical system of the boxing was gradually perfected. Apart from inheriting and improving part of the traditional Chen-style *Taiji Quan*, the Yang-style also absorbed a great deal from the other schools of boxing both with and without weapons. This

Fig. 2-4

was also due to the fact that many Wushu specialists learned from different schools of boxing and blended them together. It also showed the interchangeability of the different schools of Chinese Wushu.

The technical system of the Yang-style *Taiji Quan* is mainly composed of two parts: bare-handed boxing and boxing with weapons. They are divided into the following categories:

Boxing Routines: The nuclear content of the Yang-style *Taiji Quan* is composed of various single movements, including the various techniques of *Taiji Quan*. The training of various functions of the human body is the primary object of life enhancement and acquisition of combat skills (Fig. 2-5).

Push Hand: An exercise for two or more people, the *Taiji Quan* push hand (Fig. 2-6) is an effective way to apply *Taiji* power to improve the sensitivity of the human body, to facilitate the exchange between the body and mind and to increase combat ability. The forms of

Fig. 2-5

the Yang-style push hand include the push hand with fixed stance, and the push hand with moving stance. The push hand with fixed stance means that the push hand is executed without moving the feet, while the push hand with moving stance means that the push hand movements can be executed with the feet moved in any direction.

Taiji Sword: This is one of the weapons used in the Yang-style *Taiji Quan*. It is an application of the theory and principles to play sword routines, including pointing, cutting, upward swinging and piercing, as well as various body techniques and stances peculiar to Yang-style boxing (Fig. 2-7).

Taiji Sabre: Another weapon used in Yang-style *Taiji Quan*. To play sabre is a routine for the application of Yang-style *Taiji* theory and principles. It blends some boxing techniques into the sabre play. The *Taiji* sabre play is not as "hard as the tiger" as described in other sabre play, but it embodies hardness in softness and "hides the needle in the cotton"; it therefore has its own special characteristics (Fig. 2-8).

Taiji Spear: Spear is a common weapon used in Chinese Wushu. The *Taiji* spear is used mainly for training the *Taiji* power. When it is in play, it consists of opening, closing, twisting and turning movements executed in an imposing manner. It is an important supplementary aid for the boxing exercises.

There are also the *Taiji* seven-star rod and the *Taiji* ball.

In this book, we will mainly deal with the main nuclear content of the *Taiji Quan*—the basic routines of the Yang-style.

It is easy to learn the Yang-style *Taiji Quan* and popularize it among its enthusiasts. Many of the prevailing

Fig. 2-6

Fig. 2-7

Fig. 2-8

Taiji Quan routines are derived from the traditional routines of the Yang-style, such as the "Simplified *Taiji Quan*" and the "88-Form *Taiji Quan*."

III Basic Features

As a popular form of Chinese Wushu featuring both at internal and external exercise, the Yang-style *Taiji Quan* fully embodies the common basic elements of all Wushu schools in many aspects. For example, life enhancement is closely blended with combat, stress is laid on cleverness instead of clumsiness, and nimbleness is encouraged. However, it has its own clear characteristics which are shown in the form, energy training, power training and mind training.

1. Form—Relaxed, Soft, Upright, Continuous and Even

All the movements of the Yang-style *Taiji Quan* are executed softly like floating clouds and flowing water —not a trace of hardness. To make the movements soft, the most important thing is to relax the body parts. All movements of the Yang-style *Taiji Quan* are curve-shaped, a fact that conforms to the structure of the human body. All the joints are loosened, and every movement has its proper space. All the limbs and the torso are slightly curved when they are straight, and slightly straight when they are curved. Therefore, in the course of practising the Yang-style *Taiji Quan*, there is always a feeling of complete relaxation, from the internal organs to the external parts of the body.

The fundamental principle for the body form is "upright" in the Yang-style *Taiji Quan*. Whether in the fixed form or in motion, to keep the body upright is always a basic feature from start to finish. The theory of *Taiji Quan* emphasizes: "When standing, the body must be kept upright so as to give support in all directions," and "To keep the body upright must be the fundamental principle." To keep the body upright is needed both for life enhancement and combat. As for life enhancement, when the body is upright, the internal energy moves freely with no stoppage. When the body is in motion, the energy reaches all parts of the body; when it is still, it keeps the internal organs fit. Classical boxing theory holds that when the body is upright, the yin and yang of the body are combined, implying the action of the *Taiji* and its resultant changes. This will help the boxer to regulate the body's yin and yang effectively. As for combat, when the body is upright, the range of change is wider and the change more flexible. Therefore, it is said in boxing theory: "When the body technique is correct, the body is upright and does not slant in any direction, and the emptiness and flexibility are hidden. Therefore, there is no fear of being knocked down by others" (Fig. 3-1).

Fig. 3-1

The softness and uprightness of the body in the Yang-style *Taiji Quan* is embodied in all parts of the body:

Head: The head is up, the neck is vertical, and the lower jaw is in so that the whole head is kept erect.

Chest and back: The chest is in and the back is straight so that the upper part of the body is upright and comfortable. The chest and back are fully extended and the internal organs are relaxed to the maximum extent.

Waist and abdomen: The waist and hips are relaxed, the abdomen must not be softened, and the buttocks and waist must be kept in. The waist, which links the upper and lower parts of the body, merits special attention from those practising *Taiji Quan*.

Shoulders and elbows: The shoulders and elbows are dropped. In these exercises, both shoulders should be kept level to avoid the awkward situation in which one shoulder is high and the other is low. The elbows must always be bent slightly and must not be stiffly straight.

Groin: In the course of practice, the groin is always loose, round and empty. It must not be pressed too tightly.

Legs and feet: The legs must be clearly divided between empty and solid, and the feet must be firm. The Yongquan acupoint in the centre of the foot must be empty. In practising *Taiji Quan*, the power starts from the feet and takes shape at the fingertips.

Spine: Every joint is loosened, with the upper and lower responding to each other.

Coccyx: Hanging down.

The requirements are very detailed for every part of the body in the Yang-style *Taiji Quan*. The beginners should get to know and confirm them in the course of their practice.

Continuity and evenness constitute other major basic features of the Yang-style. It all begins with the starting form, and continues like flowing water until the closing form with no stop in between. Even in the fixed forms, there is also motion in stillness. A close connection between the different forms exists, and the whole routine is a complete set. Throughout all movements, the speed is even and remains the same from start to finish. It should not be quick at one moment and slow at another. (This is different from the Chen-style *Taiji Quan*, which calls for changes in speed).

Continuity and evenness are also shown in breathing. In the course of practice, breathing and movement should be integrated, with the speed of movement adjusted to fit the breathing.

The rhythms of Yang-style *Taiji Quan* as a whole are slow, so that the *qi* (vital energy) can be passed to the whole body. Every part of the body is open and the mind can be used to regulate the movements. This also helps to stabilize the body form and breathing.

2. Energy Training—Integration of Internal and External, and Smooth and Natural Flow

Energy training is the fundamental for internal exercise of the *Taiji Quan*, while the movement of limbs and body is an external form. To the human body, the training of the energy stream is of substantial content. The energy training for the Yang-style *Taiji Quan* is mainly shown in the following aspects:

With the integration of internal and external, the energy flows through the whole body. When one part moves, all parts move together. The external movement leads to the internal movement, which, in turn, is used to guide the external movement. As a result, the strength and the energy integrate, as do the external and internal, the upper and the lower, and the energy and the blood. All joints are connected so that the energy flows to the whole body. Some people find their whole body warm in the course of practice—an effect produced through energy training.

Limbs and body guide exercises and the mind is used to control the energy flow. The movements of the *Taiji Quan* are set according to the physiological rules of the human body, and every movement is guided by the acupuncture channels. While the limbs open or close, the Yang-style *Taiji Quan* uses the mind to control the energy. When a movement is executed, the energy arrives; when all parts of the body move, the internal energy is trained in many aspects. In a fixed form, it is required that the energy reaches the tips of the limbs. In this way, the internal energy is in harmony with the movements, so that the routine exercises include energy training from start to finish.

Energy flows to the Dantian gently and naturally. The Dantian is located in the lower abdomen and is regarded as the place for depositing vital energy. In the Chinese Qigong exercises, many follow the principle that "the energy stays at Dantian." The waist is used as the axis in the Yang-style *Taiji Quan* exercises and Dantian becomes the centre point for the whole body. In the whole movement process a sense of stability is required for the energy to flow to Dantian. In this way the internal energy will flow gently and naturally, with no disorder and impetuosity. This is to turn the practice into a process of accumulating energy instead of losing energy. After practising for some time, there will be a feeling of fullness at Dantian.

3. Power Training—Hardness Dwells in Softness, and the Process Is An Integral Whole

Taiji Quan is an art of boxing which makes clever use of all kinds of skills. It encourages the use of small force to overcome big force. If one learns it well, the weak can defeat the strong.

The movements in the Yang-style *Taiji Quan* are soft and slow, but call for hardness in the softness. It is by no means weak. The primary object of being soft is to destroy the unreasonably stiff and hard force formed in the human body in daily life. It helps to improve coordination among the muscles so that a complete force is generated in the whole body under the guidance of the consciousness; as a result, the quality of the human body will be greatly improved.

In the use of combat skills, the powerful force sometimes lacks room for change and therefore lands itself in a passive situation in the body form. Most of the Yang-style *Taiji Quan* forms are light and nimble. Whenever the body moves, the power is not exposed externally and no part of the body, the joints in particular, protrudes. This is the process of practice—from softness to hardness, and from hardness to softness.

The Yang-style encourages the use of four ounces to overcome a weight of 500 kilogrames in the power training programme. Stress is always laid on the clever use of force and attention paid on tapping the potential force in the human body to raise the efficiency in using this force. The "force" acquired through softness training is known as "power" in the *Taiji Quan*. In the Yang-style *Taiji Quan*, the "power" is mainly divided into the following categories:

Listening power: This refers to the sense of the force from outside; for example, the sensitivity to the change and strength of the power of the opponent. In combat, the proper acquirement of the listening power is the basis for the correct mechnical response. In life enhancement, it reflects the smooth passage in the body.

Neutralizing power: This refers to dealing with the force from outside; that is, to completely shift the force imposed by the opponent. So it is also called the "power shifting method." Proper learning of the neutralizing power helps to effectively control the opponent's centre of weight and puts the practitioner in an offensive position. In the training, dropping the shoulders and elbows or pulling in the chest and belly are both methods to acquire the neutralizing power.

Sticking power: This refers to the method of restraining the opponent from using his power, or "blocking" him from using his power so that he cannot find his target for attack nor hurt his partner. Circling movements and softness training are both methods of acquiring the sticking power.

Releasing power: This is also called "explosive force" in the *Taiji Quan*. Once the target is spotted, release the power of the whole body to attack the opponent. The releasing power includes both long and short releasing power.

In addition, there are also catching power, breaking power, snapping power, etc.

4. Mind Training—Consciousness Accumulation, Quietness and Emptiness

From the training of the body form to the training of the mind and will is a sublimation of the *Taiji Quan* skills. The training of the mind is the essence of the *Taiji Quan*. Ancient boxing doctrines stress: "Use the mind instead of the power"; that is, the primary attention should be paid to the training of the mind in the play of the *Taiji Quan*.

Both the movements and the energy accumulation are exercises guided by the mind. The Yang-style *Taiji Quan* calls for the integration of internal and external. The internal here means the integration of the "mind," "will" and "energy." The reason for the difference between *Taiji Quan* and other physical exercises is that it can effectively improve the function of human awareness and better improve the coordination between the mind and form in human life.

The main characteristics of mind training in the Yang-style *Taiji Quan*:

Mind collection: The expression is collected inside. The boxing form is sedate and elegant, the manner is serene and the expression in the eyes is gentle and natural. It is important not to look outside consciously nor gaze at a particular place, so that the energy can be accumulated inside, thereby reducing unnecessary loss.

Calmness: In practising the *Taiji Quan*, there must be calmness and no emotions. The mind must be concentrated so that the mind becomes one with the boxing forms at all times. Persistence in practice this way for a long time helps to coordinate the functions of the nervous system and increase the self-control ability of the cerebrum over the human body. People who persist in practising the *Taiji Quan* not only have agile bodies, but also possess quick responses from the cerebrum and strong resistance to interference from outside.

Use of the consciousness: Calmness does not mean ossification without motion. It is to seek stillness in motion. The consciousness is tempered in the course of its application. The use of the consciousness has two implications: one is to "use the consciousness to guide the energy flow" so that the energy will bulge and gather in the marrow; the other is to "use the consciousness to move the body." The meaning here is that every movement is accompanied by consciousness, or consciousness should precede the body form, or consciousness comes before a movement

27

changes. In this way, the change in the body form is flexible.

In short, the Yang-style *Taiji Quan* is a soft, upright and well-coordinated exercise for the whole human body, in which the form, energy and mind integrate under the guidance of the mind. It is good for people in all age groups and helps to prevent or cure illnesses, improve and build up health and protect people from possible assault by others.

IV Basic Knowledge

1. Basic Hand Forms

(1) Fist: The hand is clenched with the fingers doubled into the palm and the thumb doubled inward across the forefinger and the middle finger. The wrist should be relaxed and flat (Fig. 4-1). In the punch and fist throwing exercises, the hand forms are all fists (Fig. 4-2). The fist should be clenched loosely, not too tightly and stiffly.

(2) Palm: The fingers should be separated naturally. The part between the thumb and the forefinger should be round, and the centre of the palm should face inside (Fig. 4-3). The fingers should not be stiffly straight. All five fingers should be bent to a certain degree.

In the Yang-style *Taiji Quan*, the palm can be divided into the following categories:

Palm downward: The centre of the palm faces downward, such as the two palms in the starting form (Fig. 4-4).

Palm upward: The centre of the palm faces upward, such as the left and right palms in the Step Back and Whirl Arms on Both Sides (Fig. 4-5).

Standing palm: The tips of the fingers point upward, such as the upper hand in the Golden Cock Stands on One Leg (Fig. 4-6).

(3) Hook: Put the five fingers closely and naturally together, bend the wrist and relax (Fig. 4-7). In the Single Whip and Push Down in the Yang-style *Taiji Quan*, the hand forms are mostly hooks (Fig. 4-8).

Fig. 4-1

Fig. 4-2

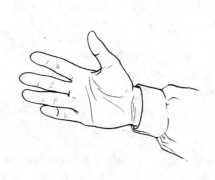

Fig. 4-3

Fig. 4-4

Fig. 4-5   Fig. 4-6

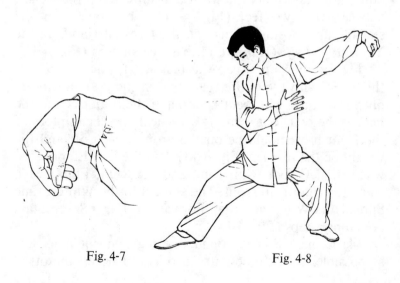

Fig. 4-7   Fig. 4-8

31

2. Basic Stances

(1) Bow Step: Keep the legs apart, one behind the other, bend the front leg and squat, keeping the rear leg naturally straight, slightly arched. Keep the tiptoes of the front foot towards the front, with the shank forming a right angle with the ground level and the knee not beyond the tiptoe. Turn the tiptoes of the rear foot slightly outward, relax the waist and "sit" on the hips. Keep both feet on the ground, with the weight on the front leg (Fig. 4-9). The bow step is the common stance used in the *Taiji Quan*. The stances used in the Brush Knee and Twist Step and Apparent Close-Up are the bow step (Fig. 4-10). It is called the Left Bow Step when the left foot is in front, and the Right Bow Step when the right foot is in front.

(2) Balance Stance: Keep the feet apart, tiptoes forward and knees slightly bent. Stand loosely and quietly. Squat a bit and relax the waist and hips. Keep the weight between the two feet (Fig. 4-11). The stances in the starting and closing forms and the Crossed Hands in the Yang-style *Taiji Quan* are all balance stances (Fig. 4-12).

(3) Empty Step: Keep the feet apart, one in front of the other, with the entire rear foot on the ground, tiptoes outward. Squat with bent knees, and the buttocks and the heel of the rear foot forming a vertical line. The tiptoes of the front foot should be on the ground, heel off and the weight on the rear leg (Fig. 4-13). It is the Left Empty Step when the left foot is in front, and the Right Empty Step when the right is in front. The stances in the White Crane Spreads Its Wings and Step Forward to Form Seven Stars are empty steps (Fig. 4-14).

(4) Crouch Stance: Bend one leg and squat as low as possible, with tiptoes turned outward. Keep the other

Fig. 4-9

Fig. 4-10

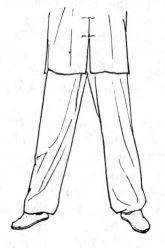

Fig. 4-11

Fig. 4-12

leg naturally straight and press it down close to the ground, tiptoes forward and slightly inward. Relax the waist and hips, and curve the crotch (Fig. 4-15). Buttocks should not be protruded in forming this stance. The stance used in the push down of the Yang-style *Taiji Quan* is the crouch stance (Fig. 4-16). This stance requires much training. People in different age groups must decide how low they should squat, according to their own physical conditions. It is a Left Crouch Stance when the left foot is in front, and a Right Crouch Stance when the right foot leads.

(5) Seated Stance: Keep the feet apart, one in front. Bend the rear leg and squat, with the whole sole on the ground and weight on the rear leg. Stretch the front leg naturally, but without tight force, heel on the ground and tiptoes off. The body should sit down slightly with the coccyx against the heel of the rear foot, the knee tip and tiptoes of the rear foot basically on the same line (Fig. 4-17). It is a Left Seated Step when the left foot is in front, and a Right Seated Step when the right foot is in front. The stance in Raise Hands and Step Forward and Hand Strums the Lute of the Yang-style *Taiji Quan* is the seated step (Fig. 4-18). Moreover, the Seated Step is often used as a transition step for changing the movements.

(6) Single-Leg Step: Stand on one leg, with the knee slightly bent. Raise the other leg with knee bent, the thigh above horizontal level, and tiptoes down (Fig. 4-19). It is the Right Single-Leg Step when standing on the right leg, and the Left Single-Leg Step when standing on the left leg. The step used in the Golden Cock Stands on One Leg and in kicking is the Single-Leg Step (Fig. 4-20).

(7) Half Horse-Riding Step: Keep the feet wide apart and squat with bent knees. Keep one leg slightly straight,

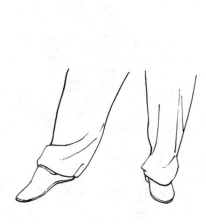

Fig. 4-13   Fig. 4-14

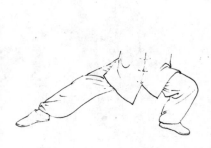

Fig. 4-15   Fig. 4-16

Fig. 4-17

Fig. 4-18

Fig. 4-19

Fig. 4-20

with weight on the other leg, and both thighs above horizontal level (Fig. 4-21). The step used in Tame Tiger with Punches for Self-Defence is the Half Horse-Riding Step (Fig. 4-22).

Stance is one of the basic skills for learning *Taiji Quan* well. In the course of practice, every stance should be executed clearly, naturally, steadily and relaxed. The changes should be flowing, light and agile.

3. Basic Hand Techniques

Hand techniques are hand movements used to coordinate the movements of the whole body. The basic hand techniques include:

(1) Upward and Outward Parry: An outwardly extended movement or a movement of the front hand. The arm is bent, with the palm inward. Move the hand up from below for an upward parry, with the force from the outer side of the arm (Fig. 4-23).

(2) Downward Parry with Both Hands: The palms face

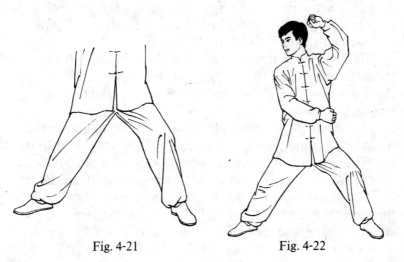

Fig. 4-21   Fig. 4-22

each other, arms bent. Move the hands downward and backward while turning the waist (Fig. 4-24).

(3) Push with Circled Arms: Keep the front arm curved, palm facing inward, and the rear palm close to the inner side of the front forearm, palm facing forward and fingers up. Push both hands forward, with the arms forming a circle (Fig. 4-25). In executing the push with circled arms, do not move the hands too far forward, in order to avoid wrong arm and wrist angles.

(4) Press: Relax and open the hands to press forward in a circular shape, as if pressing an object, palm forward, fingers up. Bend the elbow slightly, drop the shoulders and relax the waist (Fig. 4-26). The wrists should not be higher than the shoulders, and lower than the chest.

(5) Push: Extend the hands forward from behind naturally. The pushing should be executed basically along the central line of the body, not too inclined to one side. In pushing, the force originates from the feet, dominates at the waist and reaches the hands (Fig. 4-27).

(6) Plant: Plant one hand downward from above, fingers down, palm facing inside and eyes on the planting hand. Keep the thumb apart (Fig. 4-28).

(7) Part: Part the crossed or linked hands and move them to both sides, or one up and the other down. After the separation, keep the hands in opposite directions as if responding to each other (Fig. 4-29).

(8) Brush: Move one palm downward from above and past the hips and knees, and then stop it by the hip. Move the other palm in the corresponding way (Fig. 4-30).

(9) Hold: Open the hands widely and move them down from both sides, then hold them up and cross them before the chest (Fig. 4-31). In holding, keep the arms in a circular shape and away from the body. Drop the shoulders and relax the elbows.

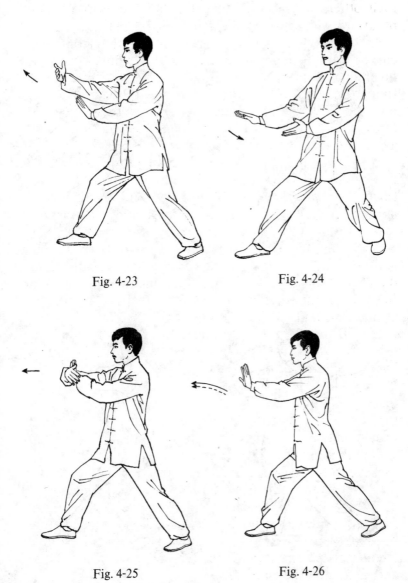

Fig. 4-23

Fig. 4-24

Fig. 4-25

Fig. 4-26

Fig. 4-27

Fig. 4-28

Fig. 4-29

Fig. 4-30

(10) Wave Hands Like Clouds: Move the hands up and down or from left to right and from right to left, alternately, in circular form. Change the directions of the palms while turning the arms. Keep the palms not higher than the head and not lower than the abdomen (Fig. 4-32).

Described above are the ten basic palm techniques. In the Yang-style *Taiji Quan*, some common fist techniques are used:

(11) Hitting Fist: Hit forward with the fist from behind, fist face forward, fist eye up (the round hole formed by thumb and forefinger). The fist centre or palm centre should face inside with eyes in the hitting direction (Fig. 4-33).

(12) Sweeping Side Punch: Hit forward with both fists. Clench the fists, move them obliquely upward from below and hit together towards the centre from outside, with the fist backs facing each other. The part to be hit is above the middle of the body (Fig. 4-34). Eyes on the centre between the two fists.

(13) Downward Punch: Hit the fist downward from above in front of the body, fist face obliquely down, fist centre inside and eyes on the hitting direction. Keep the fist level with the waist (Fig. 4-35).

(14) Swinging Punch: Swing the fist inward and upward in a circular shape from the side below and then forward. In the process of swinging, move the fist while turning the body (Fig. 4-36).

(15) Upper Fist Block: Form fists and cross the wrists in front of the body, fist face up. Keep the arms in a circle for a firm block, eyes looking ahead. The fists should be level with the chest (Fig. 4-37).

In addition to the hand techniques described above, there are also other techniques, including Leaning Against, Holding Up and Pressing Down. They are used

Fig. 4-31

Fig. 4-32

Fig. 4-33

Fig. 4-34

Fig. 4-35

Fig. 4-36

Fig. 4-37

with other techniques in the routines. It should be stressed that all techniques are part of the coordinated movements of the whole body; that is, "move the hands with the body." Any use of hand movements without the movements of the other parts of the body is incorrect.

4. Basic Steps

(1) Advance: In changing from exercise to exercise, move the front foot one step forward in front of the body (to forward left or forward right) or move the rear foot forward passing the front foot (Fig. 4-38), while placing the lead foot, land the heel first and then the whole foot.

(2) Follow-up Step: After moving one foot forward, move the other foot half a step forward, but still behind the front foot (Fig. 4-39), such as the follow-up step in the Hand Strums the Lute in the Yang-style *Taiji Quan*.

(3) Retreat: Move one foot backward to the backward left or backward right (Fig. 4-40). Generally land the toes first and then the whole foot. The steps used in the Step Back and Whirl Arms on Both Sides are retreats.

(4) Turning Step: Pivot on the heel or tiptoes to turn the foot outward or inward (Fig. 4-41). This step is often used in the body-turning movements to ensure that the body turns steadily without inclining to either side.

(5) Side Step: Move feet to either side continuously with tiptoes always forward (Fig. 4-42). This step is used in Waving Hands like Clouds.

(6) Small Step: Move one foot close to the same place, or without much change of location by tiptoes or heel. This step is used mostly for adjusting the body balance and shifting the body weight.

In addition to the six basic steps described above, there are also Back Cross-Step, Backward Step and Alternating Step. When changing the steps, the movements should be

Fig. 4-38

Fig. 4-39

Fig. 4-40

Fig. 4-41

Fig. 4-42

steady, flexible and light. Experts say: "Move the feet like a cat walking."

5. Basic Leg Techniques

Leg techniques are forms of leg movements in the air. The main leg techniques used in the Yang-style *Taiji Quan* include:

(1) Heel Kick: After raising the foot, kick it outward with the force on the heel, tiptoes flexed back while standing firmly on the supporting leg (Fig. 4-43).

(2) Toe Kick: Stand firmly on the supporting leg. Raise the other leg, bent, with force on the tiptoes and instep flat, kicking side-forward (Fig. 4-44).

(3) Lotus Kick: Stand firmly on one leg, raise the other leg toward the inner side and kick it forward before the body, instep flat, moving both hands from outside inward to beat the kicking foot (Fig. 4-45).

6. Basic Body Techniques

Body techniques are forms of body movements. The general principles for the body techniques in the Yang-style *Taiji Quan* are uprightness, firmness, full extension of the body, calmness, free movement and natural changes of movements. The basic body techniques include:

(1) Turn to Left or Right: Pivot on the waist and turn the torso to the left or right. While turning the body, move the hands forward and backward alternately in rhythm with the body turning; at the same time, pay due attention to the space on both sides.

(2) Move Obliquely: In some of the advancing movements of the Yang-style *Taiji Quan*, the practitioner does not move entirely along a straight line, but moves along an oblique line in different directions. The balance line is

Fig. 4-43

Fig. 4-44

Fig. 4-45

47

still the straight line in the middle, but there is more flexibility.

(3) Backward Turn: Although not many turning movements exist in the Yang-style *Taiji Quan*, they are significant. Keep the body upright while executing the backward turning movements and guard against twisting and impulsiveness. Be quiet in the course of the change.

(4) Rise and Fall: Keep the body weight at the same height and guard against rise and fall in most of the movements. However, the body does rise and fall in some of them. For example, in connecting the Push Down with Golden Cock Stands on One Leg, the body first falls below the average weight line and then rises above it. The location for the weight centre in the Yang-style *Taiji Quan* should be decided properly in the starting form, the height for each individual depending on his or her physical condition and habits. Generally speaking, people in good physical condition should have lower weight (not too low), and old or weak people are advised to use the high framed forms.

V Basic Techniques

Basic skills are the ladder which allows you to learn the routines well. They include methods of training the will and energy, the basic movements for adjusting the body form, and some basic single movements in the Yang-style *Taiji Quan*. Training in the basic skills helps the body and mind to reach a certain state and create favourable conditions for learning the routines.

1. Basic Stake Exercises

Stake exercises are the basis for the internal exercises of the *Taiji Quan*. When performing the still exercises, regulate the mind and breathing to feel the changes inside the body, and understand the internal rules of life.

The content of *Taiji Quan* stake exercises is very rich, and forms its own system. There are 13 stake exercises, which are called "*Taiji* 13 Stakes." In the traditional *Taiji Quan* teaching, great importance is attached to the stake exercises. A saying emphasizes: "Stand still like a stake for three years before you get the knack of it." This is because this exercise improves the internal organs and acupuncture channels, and also helps to underline the essential points in the practice of *Taiji Quan*. The following is a description of the most basic four stake exercises of *Taiji Quan*:

(1) *Wuji* (Poleless) Stake: According to *Taiji* theory, "*Wuji* gave birth to *Taiji*." *Wuji* stake exercise is the parent of *Taiji Quan*. It is a state of keeping the body quiet, empty, even and balanced. The *Wuji* Stake exercise includes the major requirements for the body forms of the *Taiji Quan*. This is why almost all schools of *Taiji Quan*

have included the *Wuji* Stake exercises as an important part of their starting and closing forms.

Description of the *Wuji* Stake exercise:

Keep the feet apart at shoulder width, tiptoes forward, and stand still and relaxed (Fig. 5-1). Keep the neck relaxed and straight so that the head is upright. Keep the Baihui acupoint at the top of the head slightly up, lower the chin slightly in. Eyes look ahead. Keep the teeth and lips closed, with the tongue touching the upper jaw. Keep the arms naturally down, relax the shoulders and drop the elbows. Don't keep the chest out too much, but draw it back a little. Draw the abdomen back slightly, keep the buttocks in, and relax the hips, with the crotch relaxed and round. Bend the kness slightly, toes relaxed and touching the ground.

Keep calm, breathe deeply like a long thread and gradually forget the breathing. The more relaxed the body, the lighter it becomes. Gradually, it seems that the body no longer exists, with a feeling of emptiness and transparency both inside and outside. Then the body feels slightly warm and this is exactly the phenomenon of "emergence of vital energy in stillness" as a result of the *Taiji* internal exercises. Keep doing the stake exercises and you will find the vital energy flowing through the whole body and yourself full of energy and in high spirits. At this moment, slowly stop looking in the distance, close the eyes, look internally at the Dantian in the small abdomen and watch Dantian silently. Make sure not to listen to, look at or smell anything. This is called "modelling the body," a method to keep vital energy strengthening the body.

When closing the form, first gradually concentrate the mind on breathing and adjust the rhythm so that the breathing is light and stable. Just imagine that all pores are open and the inside and outside of the body are naturally mixed together. While inhaling, imagine that you are drawing the natural essence of the air into the body, and while exhaling, imagine you are dispelling all the foul breath from inside the body. Repeat several times. Then close the hands at the Dantian (Fig. 5-2), and stay silent for a few moments.

(2) Horse-Riding Stake:

The Horse-Riding Stake exercise stresses increased stability of the lower parts of the body and the strength of the legs, and avoiding the flowing of the vital energy and blood upward and short breath during the practice. Persistence in doing the Horse-Riding Stake exercise helps to increase the internal force and improves the function of the lungs.

Description of the Horse-Riding Stake:

Keep the feet apart, slightly wider than the shoulders. Bend the legs and squat to a height depending on your own condition. Generally speaking, the beginners are advised to practise higher and gradually lower the height after

Fig. 5-1

Fig. 5-2

some time. Keep the body weight between the feet and the body upright. Eyes look ahead. Keep both palms facing the ground, fingers obliquely forward and by the two sides (Fig. 5-3). Keep the chest in and the back straight, drop the shoulders and elbows, and keep the coccyx upright. Keep clam and hold the expression in check. Keep the arms arched, as if holding a ball in them. Close the mouth and teeth and use the nose to breathe. After practising the Horse-Riding Stake for some time, you will find the limbs powerful and the Dantian full of vital energy.

(3) Empty and Solid Stake:

This exercise stresses the body feeling toward emptiness and solidness. In the *Taiji Quan*, every exercise is full of emptiness and solidness. The change of the body weight centre is the alternation between the empty and the solid. To strengthen the sense of emptiness and solidness makes it easier to change the boxing forms and avoid the dullness of the body.

Description of the Empty and Solid Stake:

Keep the feet together and stand relaxed and still. Move the right foot one step forward, and at the same time, bend the left leg. Keep the heel of the right foot on the ground, tiptoes off, with the weight on the left leg. Keep the upper part of the body upright, relax the waist and hips, and avoid protruding the buttocks. The tip of the nose, the tip of the left knee and tiptoes of the left foot form a straight line. The right leg is naturally straight. Arch the right arm in front of the body to chest level, palm centre inward and fingers apart. Put the left palm under the right wrist, palm centre outward and fingers up, and arch the left arm. Eyes look ahead (Fig. 5-4). Keep the mind free of thoughts and cares, with the vital energy flowing to the Dantian. You will feel all parts of the body integrate, with the shoulders, elbows, knees and hips re-

Fig. 5-3   Fig. 5-4

sponding to each other. Keep the arms in a position as if you are holding a ball.

This form implies advance, retreat and turning movements, which often appear when the forms are changed. Constant practice in this stake helps to facilitate the flow of the will and vital energy through the whole body and increase the power of the waist and legs.

(4) Bow Step Stake

Bow step is a common stance used in the fixed forms of the Yang-style *Taiji Quan*. In the Bow Step Stake, there is a clear division between yin and yang. The practitioner stands firmly, with all parts of the body fully extended in all directions. This helps to increase the sense of balance in practising the *Taiji Quan*.

Description of the Bow Step Stake:

Keep the feet together, and stand relaxed and still. Move the right foot one step forward, sole on the ground and tiptoes forward. Keep the rear leg straight, tiptoes slightly outward. Shift the body weight to the front leg and bend the front leg, shank forming a right angle with the ground, with the kneecap not beyond the tiptoes. Stretch the arms horizontally forward, palms outward, and fingers up (Fig. 5-5). Keep the upper part of the body upright, avoid inclining the body forward, and drop the shoulders and elbows, eyes looking ahead. In the mind, raise the top of the head slightly, put the hands as if on a giant imaginary ball and breathe naturally. Integrate the elbow and knee while integrating the back and the centre of the bottom of both feet, stably and freely.

2. Energy Adjusting Methods

Energy adjustment refers to adjusting the energy inside the human body to facilitate its smooth flow. In the *Taiji Quan*, energy adjustment is achieved through the adjustment of thoughts, movements and breath. There are two major breathing methods for the Yang-style *Taiji Quan*: one is to alternate the exhaling and inhaling in close

Fig. 5-5

combination with the opening and closing of the movements; the other is to breathe naturally. Usually, the two methods are used at the same time in the play of the routine exercises. Following is a description of some of the energy adjusting methods which will help to coordinate the movements and breathing and make the flow of the internal energy more smooth.

(1) Opening and Closing Method

Keep the feet apart, wider than the shoulders. Stand upright, with the Baihui point at the top of the head up and the tailbone down. Put the palms opposite each other as if holding something in front of the chest, with the arms in a circular form. Drop the shoulders and elbows (Fig. 5-6). Concentrate the mind between the palms, with closed mouth.

After standing still for a moment, imagine that the gas between the palms swells to open the arms slowly, and at the same time use the nose to inhale deeply. The idea in the mind is that the air taken in is flowing through the whole body, and the entire body is becoming lighter and lighter. Open the arms to expose the chest and abdomen simultaneously (Fig. 5-7). When the arms are withdrawn to the sides of the body, close the arms again slowly and return them to the original place as shown in Fig. 5-6. At the same time exhale the air deeply with the feeling that the whole body is closing. Repeat nine times.

(2) Bathing Method

Keep the feet apart to shoulder width. Stand relaxed and still, and breathe evenly. Move the palms slowly up from both sides, palm centres up. At the same time, keep the shoulders dropped and the elbows down, eyes looking ahead, and relax the waist and hips (Fig. 5-8). While moving the palms up, use the nose to inhale deeply. In your mind is the thought that the essence of air under the

Fig. 5-6

Fig. 5-7

Fig. 5-8

Fig. 5-9

sky is held in the palms.

The palms meet over the head, fingers pointing toward each other, and fall slowly. At the same time, use the nose to exhale deeply, thinking that air has been poured into the body and that the whole body is being bathed in a hot spring, from top to bottom, with the internal organs washed with great care. The breathing keeps pace with the movement of the hands (Fig. 5-9).

Repeat nine times. After the exercises, return the hands to the sides of the body, and stand with eyes closed for a moment.

(3) Push and Pull Method

Keep the feet apart to shoulder breadth, stand relaxed and still, arms naturally down by the sides, and breathe evenly. Move the palms slowly forward and upward to the horizontal level, palm centres down. When the palms are raised to the chest level, pull them back towards the body, and turn them upright, palm centres forward. At the same time, use the nose to inhale deeply (Fig. 5-10). When the palms return to a fist's distance from the chest, push them outward slowly. At the same time use the mouth to exhale deeply, and use the mind to carry the vital energy to the palms as if the palms were pushing a giant object (Fig. 5-11). The palms are pushed until the arms are almost relaxed and straight (but not too straight and stiff), and the elbows should be slightly bent. Repeat nine times.

This method is good for linking the acupuncture channels. If you face a big tree when you practise, and push and pull the palms toward the trunk, you will feel still better.

3. Hand Technique Training Methods

Hand techniques training is the method of enabling the hand or hands (including the arm or arms) to be nimble

Fig. 5-10   Fig. 5-11

and natural so as to reach the standards as required by Yang-style *Taiji Quan*. By practising the following exercises repeatedly, the arms will be able to keep pace with the various changes of the whole body in learning the Yang-style routines.

(1) Arm-Turning and Palm-Changing Form.

This method is used to train how to change the hands from back to palm or from palm to back and how to turn the arms in coordination with the turning of the body.

Stand relaxed and still, and keep the feet apart to shoulder breadth, eyes looking ahead (Fig. 5-12). Both arms are naturally down by the sides, palms close against the legs.

Turn the right arm outward, with the palm forward, and raise the right arm naturally forward and upward slowly, turning the palm gradually up. Raise the right palm to chest level, elbow slightly down. At the same time, raise the left hand slowly up along the left side of the body, hand on the hip with the thumb behind and the other fingers in front (Fig. 5-13).

Turn the body slowly to the right. While turning the body, turn the right arm inward so that the right palm is gradually turned downward. Withdraw the right arm back and place it in front of the chest in an arc, thumb inward and the other fingers obliquely to the left. Eyes on the right palm. In the course of executing these movements, bend the knees slightly with the hips and legs turning naturally following the body.

Raise the body slowly, turn it to the left and return to the original position. Both hands are naturally down by the sides (Fig. 5-14).

Practise the left form, reversing "right" and "left" movements. Raise the left arm, right hand on the hips, and turn the body to the left, entirely symmetrical to that described above (Fig. 5-15).

(2) Hook Raising Form

Drop the arms lightly by the sides and stand relaxed and still. Eyes look ahead.

Raise the right arm slowly on the right side, palm down. At the same time, turn the body slightly to the right, left hand remaining by the side. When the right hand is raised to the right shoulder level, turn the right palm into hook by putting the fingers together and down. Eyes on the right fingertips (Fig. 5-16).

Turn the body to the left and return to the original position. Open the right palm and withdraw it to the side.

Practise the left form in a symmetrical way. Raise the left arm, change the left hand into hook and turn the body to the left. The essential points are the same as for the right form (Fig. 5-17).

(3) Push Palm Form

In this form you push the palms alternately. It is often

Fig. 5-12

Fig. 5-13

Fig. 5-14

Fig. 5-15

used in the Brush Knee and Twist Step and some other exercises.

Stand relaxed and still, hands down by the sides of the body.

Turn both arms outward at the same time so that the palms face forward, and raise them forward and upward slowly. When they are raised to waist level, bend the elbows and draw them back, palms up, and place them by the waist side, fingers forward. Eyes look ahead (Fig. 5-18).

Raise the right palm upward slowly, and when to chest level turn the palm to face forward, pushing it forward gradually along the centre line of the body, fingers up. Eyes look ahead. The elbow of the pushed palm should also be bent a bit (Fig. 5-19).

Draw the right palm slowly to the waist side and then push the left palm. Push the palms alternately in this way. Keep the arms down by the sides after the exercises.

In practising the exercise, the palms should be turned softly and naturally, not quickly. After the palms are pushed forwards, they should be slightly cupped.

(4) Ball Holding Method

The posture of holding an imaginary ball between the palms is a transitional movement in the Yang-style *Taiji Quan* routines, which has to be learned and grasped.

Stand relaxed and still, both hands down by the sides. Eyes look ahead.

Turn the body slowly to the right. At the same time raise the right arm to the upper right, palm centre down, and place it horizontally in front of the chest. Move the left hand past below the abdomen to the right waist side, palm centre up, under the right arm. Keep the palms in opposite directions as if holding a ball between them. Eyes look between the arms (Fig. 5-20).

Fig. 5-16

Fig. 5-17

Fig. 5-18

Fig. 5-19

Squat slightly while turning the body, and keep both arms in a circular form.

Return the body to the original position and draw the hands back to the sides of the body. Do the exercise in the left symmetrical way (Fig. 5-21). Repeat the exercise. Draw back the hands to the sides and stand still.

4. Stance Training Methods

The stance training methods are used to practise the stances and footwork used in Yang-style *Taiji Quan*. The footwork of the *Taiji Quan* is the key to grasping the movements, and is therefore called the "root."

(1) Forward Step

This is used solely for practising the advancing step in Yang-style *Taiji Quan*.

Keep the feet together, and stand relaxed and still. Put hands behind the body, hands together. Shift the body weight slowly to the leg while it is bent. Raise the other leg slowly, first the heel and then the tiptoes. After stand-

Fig. 5-20

Fig. 5-21

ing firmly, move the raised leg and take a light step forward (obliquely to the side forward), landing the foot, heel first and then the whole foot. At the same time, shift the body weight forward. Move the rear leg past the inner side of the front leg and obliquely forward. Land the foot, heel first, and then shift the body weight slowly forward. Repeat in the same way (Fig. 5-22).

In changing the steps, keep the body firm before raising the foot, and the landing should be light. The upper part of the body is always upright and the whole body should be absolutely stable.

(2) Backward Step

This is used solely for practising the retreating step in the Yang-style *Taiji Quan*.

Keep the feet together, and stand relaxed and still. Put the hands behind the body, hands together. Shift the body weight slowly to one leg while it is bent down. Raise the other leg slowly, first the heel and then the tiptoes. After standing firmly, move the raised leg and take a light step backward (obliquely to the side backward), and land the foot, tiptoes first and then the whole foot. At the same time, shift the body weight backward. Move the front leg past the inner side of the rear leg and obliquely backward. Land the foot, tiptoes first and then shift the body weight slowly backward. Repeat in the same way (Fig. 5-23).

The essential points for the retreating step are the same for the advancing step. The two steps can be practised together.

(3) Side Step

This is the step used for moving the body sideways.

Stand relaxed and still, both hands on hips, upright and stable. Place the body weight between the feet. (Fig. 5-24).

Shift the body weight to the right leg, left heel off and tiptoes on the ground (Fig. 5-25). Raise the left foot, and

Fig. 5-22   Fig. 5-23

Fig. 5-24   Fig. 5-25

move it one step to the left side, tiptoes forward and whole foot on the ground. Then shift the body weight slowly to the left leg. Raise the right foot and move it to the left side, placing it by the inner side of the left foot, tiptoes on the ground (Fig. 5-26). Then shift the body weight to the right leg, the whole right foot on the ground. At the same time, raise the left heel, tiptoes on the ground. Move the left foot to the left side. Repeat the previous movements. In this way, shift the body weight back and forth between the two legs, but continue to move the body to the left.

Stand relaxed and still, and do the Right Side Step exercise (Figs. 5-27–28).

(4) One-Leg Step

This exercise is used for practise balance on one leg.

Place both hands on the hips, and stand relaxed and still.

Shift the body weight to the left leg, knee slightly bent. Bend the right leg and raise it, tiptoes naturally down. Keep the body upright and avoid shaking it back and forth. This is the Left One-Leg Step.

Put the right leg down slowly. At the same time, shift the body weight to the right leg, knee slightly bent. Bend the left leg and raise it to form the Right One-Leg Step. Put down the left leg, and raise the right leg. Repeat the exercise in this way. Each One-Leg Step should be kept for a moment (Fig. 5-29).

(5) Bow-Empty Step

This is an exercise for interchange between the bow step and empty step.

Place both hands on the waist, and stand relaxed and still.

Move the right foot a big step forward, heel first on the ground and then the whole foot. Shift the body weight forward to form the Right Bow Step (Fig. 5-30).

Fig. 5-26

Fig. 5-27

Fig. 5-28

Fig. 5-29

Fig. 5-30

Fig. 5-31

Shift the body weight slowly backward to the left leg, bend the left knee. At the same time, raise the right heel, tiptoes on the ground, pull the foot back lightly and place it in front of the left foot to form the Right Empty Step (Fig. 5-31).

Place the whole right foot on the ground. Shift the body weight forward to the right leg. Raise the left foot and move it one step forward, first heel on the ground and then gradually the whole foot, shifting the body weight forward to form the Left Bow Step. Shift the body weight backward to the right leg, pull the left foot back to form the Left Empty Step. Repeat the exercises by alternating the steps in this way.

5. Body Improving Exercises

Body improving exercises are exercises for the basic movements designed to achieve the basic physical qualities required by the play of the *Taiji Quan*. The activities include exercises for body techniques and footwork.

(1) Bending Forward and Backward:

Keep the feet apart, and stand relaxed and still.

Put the palms on the small of the back, bending the body slowly backward to the maximum (Fig. 5-32). While bending the body backward, bend the knees slightly, and use both hands to push and press the back. Press the elbows slightly backward to help push the abdomen forward. Keep the stance for about half a minute.

Raise the body slowly, stand for a moment, and then bend the body forward to the maximum (Fig. 5-33). While bending the body, do not bend the knees, but relax the toes. Put both palms down to press the ground. Keep the stance for half a minute before rising slowly to stand erect. Raise the head first, then the shoulders, and then the waist. Raise step by step.

Fig. 5-32   Fig. 5-33

Repeat the exercise several times. Inhale while bending backward, and exhale while bending forward. Use the nose to inhale, and the mouth to exhale.

(2) Waist-Turning Exercises

Keep the feet apart, wider than the shoulders. Put both hands on the hips, body upright (Fig. 5-34). Pivot on the waist and turn the body slowly to the left, right knee slightly turned inward, with the toes of both feet grabbing the ground to help turn the waist to the maximum limit. In the course of twisting the waist, both the upper part of the body and the head are turned back naturally, with the eyes looking back as much as possible (Fig. 5-35). Keep the body upright, and maintain the stance for half a minute before returning the body slowly to the original state. Turn the waist to the right in a symmetrical way (Fig. 5-36). Repeat the exercises several times. Inhale when turning, and exhale when returning to the original state.

(3) Squatting Exercises

Fig. 5-34

Fig. 5-35

Fig. 5-36

Fig. 5-37

Keep the feet apart, wider than the shoulders, and stand relaxed and still. Keep both palm centres down, fingers forward (Fig. 5-37). Keep the thumbs wide apart from the other fingers, relax the shoulders and drop the elbows. Stand upright. Inhale deeply, close the mouth and then bend the knees to squat, with the toes grabbing the ground. Press both hands down simultaneously as if pressing a ball to the ground. In squatting, avoid protruding the buttocks. Keep the neck upright, eyes looking horizontally. Keep the stance for about half a minute before relaxing and rising slowly. Exhale from the mouth slowly after standing firmly. Repeat the exercises several times.

This exercise helps to strengthen the power of the lower limbs and improve the functions of the lungs.

6. Single Exercises

Single exercises are basic exercises selected from the Yang-style *Taiji Quan* for separate practice. They include the many essential points for learning the Yang style. Repeated practice can help you to grasp the basic content quickly.

(1) Single Whip

Single Whip, which is used many times in the routines of Yang-style *Taiji Quan*, is one of the most basic movements. In the Single Whip, you are required to stand upright, with one hand in palm and the other in hook. Open them in the air, one above and the other below. This shows the full extension of the body parts in the Yang-style *Taiji Quan*.

Keep the feet apart, about to shoulder width, and stand relaxed and still (Fig. 5-38). Raise both arms slowly from the body, palm centres down, and inhale slowly through the nose while raising the arms. Raise the palms to shoulder level, and avoid shrugging the shoulders (Fig. 5-39). Shift the body weight slowly to the right. At the same time, pivot on the waist and turn the body slightly to the right. In turning the body, place the left palm inward near the right elbow, eyes on the right hook. Raise the left heel naturally, tiptoes on the ground in an empty step (Fig. 5-40)

Move the left foot one step to the left, heel on the ground first, and then shift the body weight slowly to the left leg, the whole foot on the ground. Keep the right leg slightly straight to form the Left Bow Step. Turn the body to the left while moving the step, and move the left palm from the body in a curved shape to the left. Turn the palm and press it forward, palm centre obliquely out, and fingers up (Fig. 5-41).

Shift the body weight to the right leg and draw the left leg back, hands naturally down. Return to the still and relaxed standing position (Fig. 5-42). Do the exercises on the right side in a symmetrical way, and repeat the exercises several times.

(2) Brush the Knee with Twist Step

This is also a basic movement in the Yang-style *Taiji Quan*, which appears many times in the routines. In this exercise, the hands and feet move in a coordinated way, and there should be a strong sense of movement of the whole body.

Stand relaxed and still (Fig. 5-43). Shift the body wight slowly to the right leg, turn the body slightly to the right, and raise the right palm in a curved form from below to the upper right, palm outward and slightly above the shoulders. At the same time, place the left palm obliquely up, and move it in a curved line past the chest to the upper right, parallel to the right arm, palm centre outward. Eyes on the right palm (Fig. 5-44). Raise the left heel, toes on

73

Fig. 5-38

Fig. 5-39

Fig. 5-40

Fig. 5-41

Fig. 5-42

Fig. 5-43

Fig. 5-44

Fig. 5-45

the ground.

Move the left foot one step forward, heel first on the ground. Shift the body weight slowly forward to land the whole foot on the ground, and bend the right leg slightly to form the Left Bow Step. At the same time, move the left palm past the chest downward to brush down to the lower left past the knee, palm centre down and press it in front of the left hip. Bend and push the right arm forward by the side of the ear. Eyes follow the right palm and look ahead (Fig. 5-45).

Withdraw both hands and feet and return to the original position. Then do the right symmetrical exercise and repeat several times.

(3) Heel Kick

Heel kick is one of the major leg techniques in the Yang-style *Taiji Quan*. It is used mostly for improving the power of the lower limbs and the stability of the body.

Stand relaxed and still (Fig. 5-43). Cross the hands and move them upward slowly to the front of the chest, left hand inside and right hand outside. At the same time, shift the body weight to the left leg, bend the right leg and raise it up, tiptoes down. Eyes on the crossing (Fig. 5-46).

Turn the palms inside out, push them to both sides and stretch the arms. At the same time, kick the right foot slowly to the forward left, with the force point on the heel. Keep the right arm and right leg on the same place, elbow against the knee, and wrist against the ankle. Eyes look ahead at the right palm (Fig. 5-47).

Land the foot, withdraw the hand and return to the original position. Then do the left symmetrical exercise. Repeat the exercises several times.

(4) Wave Hands Like Clouds

In this exercise use the waist to move the body and use the body to move the hands so as to improve the unity and

Fig. 5-46

Fig. 5-47

coordination of the movements of the body parts.

Stand relaxed and still (Fig. 5-43). Raise hands slowly upward in front of the body to chest level. Shift the body weight slowly to the left leg, right heel off the ground and squat slightly. At the same time, turn the left palm outward, and move it in a curve to the left side. Move the right palm inward, to the upper right, to the lower left and obliquely down, placing it under the left elbow. Turn the body slightly to the left, eyes on the left palm (Fig. 5-48).

Move the right foot a small step horizontally to the left, whole foot on the ground. Shift the body weight slowly to the right, and move the left foot a step to the left. At the same time, pivot at the waist and turn the body to the right. Move the right hand in a curved line to the upper right, palm centre out. Move the left hand from the left downward and past the abdomen to the right in a curved line, palm in, and eyes on the right palm (Fig. 5-49).

77

Shift the body weight to the left leg, pivot at the waist and turn the body to the left, right tiptoes up. Move both hands in curved lines. Move the left palm from the lower right upward in a curved line, and past the body and to the left again, palm in. Turn the right palm out and move it down in a curved line and then again past the abdomen to the left. Eyes on the left palm (Fig. 5-50).

Move the right foot one step horizontally to the left, tiptoes on the ground, as shown in Fig. 5-48. Repeat the exercises, continuing to move to the left.

Withdraw both the hand and foot, and do the symmetrical exercise on the right.

(5) Step Back and Whirl Arms on Both Sides

This exercise is a backward step movement in the Yang-style *Taiji Quan*. Open and close the hands alternately and turn the body to the left and to the right.

Stand relaxed and still (Fig. 5-43). Shift the body weight to the right leg, turn the body slightly to the left, raise the left foot and land it to the left, tiptoes on the ground. Raise both hands upward from the two sides, and turn them outward while raising the hands so that the palms are turned up to shoulder level. Eyes on the right palm (Fig. 5-51).

Raise the left foot and move it backward to the left, tiptoes on the ground first, and then shifting the body weight to the left leg, the whole foot on the ground. Turn the body to the left at the same time. Push the right hand, elbow bent, forward past the side of the ear, palm down, left palm up. Withdraw it backward in a curved line along the right arm, and raise it from below to the left and upward. When the hands are almost extended, turn the arms outward at the same time so that the palms are up. Eyes on the left palm (Fig. 5-52).

Do the symmetrical right step backward, and turn the

Fig. 5-48

Fig. 5-49

Fig. 5-50

Fig. 5-51

body to the right. Move the hands forward and backward alternately. Repeat the exercises several times.

(6) White Crane Spreads Its Wings

Stand relaxed and still (Fig. 5-43). Raise the arms slowly forward and upward to shoulder level, shoulders dropped and elbows relaxed. Shift the body weight to the right leg, and bend the knee slightly. Raise the left foot and move it a step forward, tiptoes on the ground, to form the Left Empty Step. At the same time, extend the right hand in a curved line to the upper right, palm centre outward, to the forehead level. Press the left hand in a curved line to the lower left, palm centre down, to the front of the left hip. Keep the head and body upright, eyes looking ahead (Fig. 5-53). Relax the chest while opening the arms, and avoid shrugging the shoulders while raising the right arm.

Withdraw both hands and feet and return to the original position. Then do the symmetrical right exercise. Repeat the exercises several times.

Fig. 5-52   Fig. 5-53

VI   How to Learn the Yang-Style
Taiji Quan

Taiji Quan is a sport which scientifically develops the various components inside and outside the human body and improves coordination of the whole body. It is an ideal physical fitness exercise practised by people at most health levels and all age groups. Its range of activity can be properly regulated and controlled by enthusiasts, with a wide range of physical conditions. Its movements are designed so that the people find both physical and mental pleasure in practising them. Therefore, it is not difficult to learn *Taiji Quan*. As long as you practise deligently, you will be able to do it well. In this chapter, I take the opportunity to make a few more points in order to help my readers learn the Yang-style *Taiji Quan* more quickly and thoroughly.

1. Practise Repeatedly and Accumulate the Experience Step by Step

At the beginning, some people find themselves unable to adapt to some of the movements. This is part of the process. The situation will become better after repeated practice for some time. In some exercises requiring high degree of coordination, you might find it difficult to think of the legs while attending to the hands or to pay attention to this movement while practising that movement. If this is the case, you should execute the movements slowly or divide them into small parts and then, practise them repeatedly one by one, until the movements become fixed in your mind and you are naturally responsive to them. Then, when you practise more quickly, you will also do them more skillfully. At the beginning, you should perform separate exercises for some time everyday. After you learn the routines, you are advised to persist in doing the complete exercises, from start to finish, continuously.

2. Start with the Basic Skills and Pay Attention to the Basic Training

The play of the Yang-style *Taiji Quan* routines is continuous and cleverly varied. However, all its routines are composed of single movements which include basic hand techniques and footwork. Therefore, the beginners should first learn what is described in Chapter Four and Chapter Five of this book, and repeatedly practise the basic hand forms, stances, hand techniques, and footwork. All these basic movements are fundamental to the more advanced routines in the *Taiji Quan*. You should execute these basics very skillfully.

The stake exercises are the skills of the *Taiji Quan* for "internal training." They are a special means of training designed to integrate the mind, vital energy and force of the human body. To learn the stake exercises well will enable you to get the flavour and feelings in the practice of the routine exercises. The beginners should first practise the stake exercises separately, and after some time, practise the combinations of the stakes and movements. Even if you have learned all the routines, you should not abandon the stakes, but persist in practising them with the routines. In Chapter Five, the book also describes the methods of practising the single exercises of the most basic movements, which are intended to help you to coordinate the body parts and know the laws of movement in the Yang-style *Taiji Quan*. Before learning the routines, repeated practice of these basic exercises will be of great benefit.

3. Execute the External Forms Well

The movements in the Yang-style *Taiji Quan* have been well-designed after repeated changes. Only correct movements can produce good effects. The beginners should first imitate the movements carefully and improve them by comparison with those in the illustrations. The external forms should not deviate from the illustrations. The fixed movements are the summaries of this form and serve as transitions to the advanced movements. Therefore, special attention should be paid to them. First of all, you should know where the body weight is and clearly distinguish the empty from the solid. Second, you should decide the direction which your body faces. Third, you should correctly locate the hands and their spaces, including the spaces to the right and left, up and down, and the palms. Moreover, you should not belittle the importance of the direction of your eyes. Attention should be paid to the external forms of the moving postures: the direction and size of your step, the lines of movement of your hands (where you start and where you stop), the process of changes in body weight (weight transition in the Yang-style *Taiji Quan* is slow and even, and does not allow for rapid changes), and the sequence of changes in the body forms. In executing the external forms well, the beginners should pay attention to another basic question; that is, the hand form and stance for every exercise should be correctly performed.

4. Improve the Practice of the Routines by Stages

At the beginning of learning the routines, you should not do everything at the same time. It is very important to prepare a reasonable program for the practice. Generally

83

speaking, the study of the Yang-style *Taiji Quan* routines can be divided into three stages. In each stage, you should grasp some focal points, and at the same time, learn some other exercises.

In the first stage, you should learn the separate forms well, and on this basis, connect the separate forms into one routine. In this stage, also, it is required that the postures be correct and the body upright. A clear distinction should be made between the empty and the solid. There must be natural breathing, skillful movements, even speed and firm weight.

In the second stage, further grasp the rules for the movements of the Yang-style *Taiji Quan*, and understand its flavour and style. In this stage, you must seriously study the characteristics of the power in each form, play each complete routine naturally and smoothly, and ensure that all body parts are well-coordinated. The movements should be round, lively and relaxed, and the changes light, nimble and steady. For this reason, special attention should be paid to the principal body parts and principal links.

The principal body parts: head, shoulders, elbows, feet, waist and buttocks.

The principal links: (1) The change from one form to another—natural and clear; (2) the changes in breathing when opening and closing—the natural changes in breathing accompany the opening and closing of the movements and they should be harmonious to each other; (3) correct placing of hands and feet—the posture in every form should be fully extended, and at the same time, the stiffness of the body forms resulting from straight joints should be avoided; and (4) distribution of power—understand that the power originates from the feet, dominates at the waist, and reaches the fingers.

In the third stage, integrate the internal and the external, and unite the mind, vital energy and form. *Taiji Quan* is a sport in which the mind is used to guide the movements. In this stage, first move in the mind, and then move in the form. This means that before every movement is executed, the mind guides the line of movement and form. In practising the boxing, you should have a calm mind and concentration, and understand the characteristics of the vital energy flow and the good coordination between the movements and breathing. In this stage, because you now know the movements very well, you should give up the conscious exertion of force in executing the movements. Instead use the mind to guide the movements, in other words, "use the mind, not the physical strength." This will upgrade the movements of the body parts to the "exercises of thinking." This stage is the level of high-grade skills of *Taiji Quan*, which calls for persistent practice for a long time followed by constant improvement.

5. Combine Theory with Practice

Taiji Quan is a sport guided by *Taiji* theory. Its changes embody the philosophical mode of thinking. To know some background will help you understand it still more deeply and desire to learn more. Moreover, *Taiji Quan* also is closely related to Chinese traditional medicine. For example, the Daoyin exercises for life enhancement embody the laws of the composition of the acupuncture channels and the ideas of nourishing the internal organs. Therefore, I suggest that you get to know some theory about *Taiji Quan* in order to grasp the boxing art in still greater depth. It will serve as a good companion for both your entertainment and physical training.

VII Illustrated Exercises

This book is about the traditional routines of the Yang-style *Taiji Quan*. In order to make it easier for readers to learn the *Taiji Quan*, I have left out some repetitions and compiled the exercises properly. It is my hope that this will benefit the beginners.

Some exercises involve more changes, and are therefore divided into parts, marked as "Part I," "Part II," etc. This makes the descriptions still clearer and easier to read and practise. However, it should be noted that the divided parts are still connected into one complete exercise. No break or pause should take place in the process of practice.

1. Names

Preparatory Form
(1) Starting Form
(2) Grasp Peacock's Tail
(3) Single Whip
(4) Raise Hands and Push Up
(5) White Crane Spreads Its Wings
(6) Brush Left Knee with Twist Step
(7) Play the Pipa
(8) Brush Left and Right Knees with Twist Step
(9) Parry and Punch with Forward Step
(10) Apparent Close Up
(11) Crossed Hands
(12) Return to Mountains with Tiger in Arms
(13) Punch under Elbow
(14) Drive Monkeys Back from Left and Right
(15) Oblique Flying

(16) Brush Left Knee with Twist Step
(17) Needle at Sea Bottom
(18) Flash the Arms
(19) Turn Around and Punch
(20) White Snake Thrusts Out Tongue
(21) Oblique Flying
(22) Grasp Peacock's Tail
(23) Single Whip
(24) Wave Hands Like Clouds
(25) Single Whip
(26) Pat High on Horse
(27) Kick Out with Right Foot
(28) Strike Opponent's Ears with Both Fists
(29) Kick Out with Left Foot
(30) Right Heel Kick with Body Turn
(31) Beat Tiger from Left
(32) Beat Tiger from Right
(33) Part Wild Horse's Mane
(34) Jade Girl Works at Shuttles
(35) Push Down
(36) Golden Cock Stands on One Leg
(37) Strike Down with Forward Step
(38) Grasp Peacock's Tail with Forward Step
(39) Single Whip
(40) Push Down
(41) Step Forward to Form Seven Stars
(42) Mount Tiger with Backward Step
(43) Lotus Kick with Body Turn
(44) Bend Bow to Shoot Tiger
(45) Parry and Punch
(46) Apparent Close Up
(47) Crossed Hands
(48) Finishing Form

2. Illustrated Exercises

Preparatory Form

The preparatory form is the state of the body prepared for starting the exercises. It includes the adjustment of the different parts of the body to the state of feeling, and the still and relaxed state of mind as required for *Taiji Quan* exercises.

Method of Practice

Keep the feet naturally apart to about shoulder breadth, soles on the ground. This makes you feel comfortable and makes it easy to relax. Keep the body upright, head slightly up and lower jaw in. Put the hands naturally down by the sides, fingers relaxed and straight, and palms inward and lightly against the outer side of the thighs. Relax the waist and hips, crotch relaxed and round. All joints of the body must be relaxed. Lower the shoulders slightly, and close the mouth lightly, with the tongue at the upper jaw. Eyes look ahead, expression kept inside. Keep calm and expel all distracting thoughts from the mind (Figs. 7-1-2).

Essential Points

(1) The book *On Taiji Quan* says: "*Wuji* gave birth to *Taiji Quan*." The preparatory form is also called the "*Wuji* Position." It guides the execution of the whole set of exercises and should be done well and earnestly.

(2) After executing the external forms of the movements, relax the internal organs, step by step, to feel that the external and internal of the body are connected. A supplementary method is first to inhale deeply and then exhale evenly and mildly with the result that the body becomes relaxed and still.

(3) When standing in the preparatory form, the upper

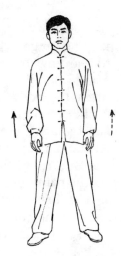

Fig. 7-1   Fig. 7-2

and lower parts of the body should be combined into a single whole to give a sense of integrity.

(4) While lowering the shoulders and relaxing the arms, do not press the armpits too tightly, nor press the palms against the legs forcefully. Keep the fingers down.

(5) The whole posture should be symmetrical and even. Keep both body and mind still, with movement implied in the stillness.

(1) Starting Form

The starting form is the first exercise of the *Taiji Quan*, in which the arms rise and fall once to complete a cycle of breathing. Because the hands begin to move with a clear distinction between yin and yang, the process is regarded in *Taiji* theory as: "*Taiji* gave birth to the two poles."

Method of Practice

Turn both hands slightly inward, backs of the hands

facing outside.

Open the fingers lightly and move the arms slowly forward and upward, palms down. Use the nose to inhale evenly and mildly, and in the mind carry the breath throughout the body. Keep the palms apart to shoulder breadth (Fig. 7-3).

When the arms are raised to shoulder level, relax the shoulders and drop the elbows. Then press the palms slowly downward, at the same time exhaling lightly.

Press the palms evenly to the hip level, fingers forward, with the parts between the thumbs and forefingers opposite each other. In the mind, all the air channels are open.

Eyes look ahead, with natural expression (Fig. 7-4).

Essential Points

(1) Keep the wrists relaxed and flat while raising the arms upward, and avoid handing the fingers down too much as a result of relaxation. In practising *Taiji Quan*, it should be stressed that the "vital energy reaches the tips of the four limbs" so that it can flow throughout the body.

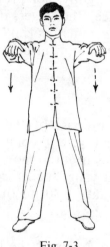

Fig. 7-3

Fig. 7-4

The internal energy swells with the movement of the external form so as to make the energy flow and blood circulation smooth. If the wrists "break," the energy flow is not smooth.

(2) Keep the body weight always between the feet.

(3) While pressing the palms down, keep the palms slightly cupped, as if holding balls and pressing them into the water slowly. After practising for a long time, you will find a sense of resistance on the hands.

(4) When the palms are pressed to waist level, relax the lower abdomen at the same time, with the mind also on the abdomen. This is called the "solid abdomen."

(5) Avoid shrugging the shoulders while raising the palms. The dropping of the palms should be soft and light. Both arms should be curved and they should not be too stiff and straight. When the palms are dropped to the hip level, the wrists should be slightly out.

The starting form for *Taiji Quan* is very important. It strikes the keynote for the whole set of exercises. The method of combining the movements with breathing, the speed of moving the arms and the sense of breath when the arms rise and fall are all applied in the consecutive exercises. This exercise should be practised repeatedly.

The breathing in the following exercises uses the nose to inhale and the mouth to exhale.

(2) Grasp Peacock's Tail

This exercise is so called because it looks as if you are using a hand to grasp a peacock's tail. Grasp Peacock's Tail is one of the most representative exercises in the Yang-style *Taiji Quan*. It includes the basic hand techniques like holding, upward parry, downward parry, circled arm pushing and parting, and the basic stances, like side bow step, seated stance, bow step, empty step, and half horse-riding stance. Therefore, many *Taiji Quan* tutors insist on compiling and composing this exercise separately so that their students can practise it repeatedly. In the traditional routines of the Yang-style *Taiji Quan*, this exercise is included several times and should be practised in different directions.

Yang Chengfu, master of Yang-style boxing, described this exercise as the "general explanation for the *Taiji Quan* exercises and their execution."

"Peacock's tail" here is likened to the human arm. The name of the exercise indicates that the internal changes in the whole body are embodied in the changes in the external forms of the arms.

Method of Practice

Part I: Squat slightly, lower the body weight gradually and then shift it to the left leg. Pivot on the heel of the right foot, tiptoes off the ground, and turn to the right side about 45 degrees. At the same time, move the right hand upward and past the chest to the right side in a curved line, palm down. Move the left hand, palm inside, past the abdomen in a curved line to the right and under the right palm, left palm up. Place the palms in a position as if holding a ball between them, right palm down (Fig. 7-5). Inhale slowly while turning the body and moving the arms. In your mind, you are holding the vital energy together. All joints in the body should be closed.

Essential Points

(1) All movements in *Taiji Quan* are coordinated movements of the whole body, and separate movements of the hands and feet are opposed. Therefore, movement of both hands to the right and the turning of the right foot should be kept in harmony with the turning of the body to the right. It is the "body which guides the movement of the hands." In this exercise, the palm down is yin while the

palm up is yang, and the two palms are kept in opposite directions, one above and the other below. This is based on the idea that yin and yang are held together, and the spirit and vital energy are kept together.

(2) While turning the body, keep the central axle of the body upright.

(3) Make the parts between the thumbs and the forefingers of both hands as wide as possible, all fingers natural and relaxed.

Method of Practice

Part II: Shift the body weight to the right leg, right sole on the ground. Move the left foot lightly up and one step to the left side (the direction you face in the preparatory form), and land the heel first on the ground and then, gradually, the whole foot. Shift the body weight slowly to the left leg, and straighten the right leg, slightly bent, to form a Left Bow Step. While shifting the body weight, turn the body slightly to the left, at the same time separating the hands. Extend the left arm upward to the

Fig. 7-5

Fig. 7-6

93

outside in a curved shape. Place the palm down behind the waist and hips. Eyes look ahead.

Exhale slowly during the whole process. In the mind, all the bones and muscles in the whole body are opened, with the vital energy reaching the tips of all limbs (Fig. 7-6).

Essential Points

(1) The upward parry is a basic technique in Yang-style *Taiji Quan*. While executing the movement, extend the outer side of the arm and the back of the hand outward with the aid of the body and legs. Upward parry should be kept in harmony with the body turning and heel kick. Keep the back upright and the body steady.

(2) While moving the left arm upward to ward off the attack from an imaginary opponent, do not raise the left elbow. In the fixed form as shown in Fig. 7-5, drop the shoulders and relax the elbows and the hips.

(3) Place the left tiptoes obliquely forward and point the right fingers to the direction the body faces.

(4) Put the left palm to about the shoulder level.

(5) Turn the right leg slightly outward.

Method of Practice

Part III: Shift the body weight slowly back to the right leg, and turn the body slightly to the right. Raise the left tiptoes, turn them to the outer side at 45 degrees, and then place them firmly on the ground. Then shift the body weight to the left leg and turn the body to the left slightly. Use the waist to move the leg, and use the leg to raise the right foot slowly. At the same time, use the body to move the arms. Move the left arm to left side in a curved shape and turn the forearm while moving, slightly down, and place it horizontally in front of the chest, palm obliquely outside. Move the right arm, palm inside, together with the right foot, in the same direction and past the abdomen to hold an imaginary object under the left palm.

Move the right foot and place it in front of the left foot, tiptoes on the ground, to form a Right Empty Step (Fig. 7-7). Eyes look under the left elbow. Inhale slowly in the whole process, with the idea that the whole body is immersed in water to produce a sense of integrity with the surroundings.

Essential Points

(1) The turning of the arms and palms should be natural and in harmony with the movement of the body. In other words, the turning of the hands is completed when the body movement is finished.

(2) Turn the body in round movements with the spinal column as the axle. The turning should be round and natural. No force should be exerted.

(3) The movement of the right foot should be light. Do not rub it on the ground. The landing should be firm and steady. Sit the body down slightly at the same time. There should be clear distinction between empty and solid steps.

(4) Keep one arm vertical and one arm horizontal, as if holding a ball in the air. This helps to produce the effect of "holding the energy" inside the body and massaging the internal organs.

Method of Practice

Part IV: Move the right foot lightly forward, and land the heel first on the ground and then the whole foot slowly. Straighten the left leg slightly and shift the body weight forward to form the Right Bow Step. At the same time, push the right arm upward from below and outward from inside in a curved shape, palm inside. This is also called upward parry (Right Upward Parry). While executing the movement of upward parry, the force should be exerted evenly with the idea of pushing a heavy object forward. Press the left arm slightly down from the inner side of the right arm and push it forward, palm outside and under the right wrist. Eyes look ahead (Fig. 7-8).

While placing the right foot firmly on the ground, turn the body slightly, front forward. Exhale mildly in the whole process, with the idea that the vital energy flows to Dantian and the whole body is round as if pushing a boat on the river smoothly and naturally.

Essential Points

(1) The pushing of the arm and the straightening of the left leg should be harmonious. The power is sent from the foot bottom, through the waist and to the hands. This is called the "flow of the power" or "free movement of the power" in *Taiji Quan*.

(2) The forearm should not be too straight. In executing the upward parry movement, use the outer side of the right arm and the back of the right hand, wrist relaxed and flat. Do not push the left palm forward too much so as to avoid inclining the body forward.

(3) Place the right palm above the right knee, not too.

Fig. 7-7   Fig. 7-8

far forward. The central line of the body is in the centre between the feet. Keep the left arm away from the body so as not to press the chest.

Method of Practice

Part V: Turn the body slightly to the right, and turn the arms with the body: the right arm inward, palm down, and the left arm outward, palm up. The palms face each other obliquely in opposite directions, left palm under the inner side of the right elbow. Eyes look at the front hand. Inhale lightly while turning the arms (Fig. 7-9).

Essential Points

(1) Move the arms slightly forward while turning them outward, but not too much upward, the right hand not higher than the top of the head.

(2) Keep the distance between the feet unchanged, but twist the legs slightly to the right with the hips and the body.

Methods of Practice

Part VI: Sit back with the whole body, body weight shifted to the left leg, and drop the elbows gradually. Pivot at the waist and turn the body to the left. Move the hands downward and to the left with the body turn for the downward parry. Eyes follow the movement of the hand (Fig. 7-10). Breathe naturally in the whole process, with the idea that the body is moving as if in a breeze, lightly and nimbly.

Essential Points

(1) While shifting the body weight backward, do not protrude the buttocks. While executing the downward parry, relax the shoulders and drop the elbows, but avoid leaning the body backward. Keep the arms away from the chest, otherwise the opponent is apt to approach your body in combat. It is also not good for life enhancement.

(2) Use the waist power to strengthen the arm power.

Fig. 7-9   Fig. 7-10

It is not advisable to use the arms only.

(3) Keep the distance between the hands almost unchanged, and avoid moving one hand quickly and the other slowly. They should respond to each other at all times.

(4) Relax the chest in the whole process. Move the internal energy downward with the execution of the downward parry, and avoid moving the feet.

Methods of Practice

Part VII: Continue to turn the body to the left, and move the arms downward. When the left palm is moved to the front of the left chest and the right palm to the front of the right chest, move the arms upward to the left in a curved shape. Turn the eyes to look at the left hand and inhale deeply. Then use the left foot to press the ground slightly and begin to turn the body back to the right, shifting the body weight slowly to the right leg. Turn the left arm inward so that the left palm is turned outward and pressing against the right wrist (Fig. 7-11).

Essential Points

(1) The locus of the upward movement of the two arms from below to the upper left is a curve. There must be no dead corners.

(2) The turning of the left arm should be round and natural. It should be turned while it is moved upward to avoid the mistake of moving the arm upward first before turning it (a common mistake for many beginners).

(3) Eyes follow the movement of the left hand.

(4) When the hands meet, the arms form a circle, which is pushed outward to be round, not oblate.

(5) The meeting point of the hands is located at about the central line of the body, not too far back nor too far forward. If it is too far back, the frame will be in disorder. If it is too far forward, it will affect the following movement.

Methods of Practice

Part VIII: Place the left hand on the right wrist. Continue to shift the body weight to the right, and continue to turn the body to the right. Push the arms to the right forward with the aid of the force of the whole body. Press the left foot against the ground to increase the force and to form the Right Bow Step. Turn the body to the right front, and push the hands to the forward front, eyes on the palms. In your mind, you are pushing away an object. Exhale slowly while turning the body and pushing the hands. When the movement is completed, the exhaling stops (Fig. 7-12).

Essential Points

(1) When pushing the hands outward, exert the force on the outer side of the right arm. The right arm should not be pushed higher than the shoulders. Keep the arms in a circle, chest relaxed and empty.

Fig. 7-11   Fig. 7-12

(2) Do not bend the body too much forward, but keep the body upright in the fixed form.

(3) Form a right angle between the right shank and the ground surface, so that the right knee is not beyond the tiptoes. Keep the right foot vertical and forward with its extension line through the left heel.

(4) Point the right fingers towards the left and the left fingers upward.

Methods of Practice

Part IX: Turn the right arm inward, palm down. At the same time, roll the left hand forward along the right wrist, palm also turned down. Move the hands apart to both sides, shift the body weight backward, and at the same time, drop the elbows and draw the arms back, palms down. Eyes look at the palms. While sitting backward, turn the body slightly to the left. While the hands are withdrawn, inhale the air into the lower abdomen (Fig. 7-13).

Essential Points

(1) When the palms are drawn back, they must not be too close to the body. Keep the front leg bent to a certain degree, and relax the hips when sitting backward.

(2) When the hands are drawn back, they must be placed at the central line of the body and not inclined to one side. The thumbs must be pitted against the centres of the breasts—which is called "central Dantian" in the internal exercise of Wushu.

Methods of Practice

Part X: Shift the body weight forward to form the Right Bow Step. At the same time, press-push the palms forward horizontally in a curved shape, fingers up and the parts between the thumbs and forefingers opposite each other. Place the palms to shoulder level. Eyes look ahead (Fig. 7-14). Exhale while pressing the palms with the idea of pushing a giant balloon.

Essential Points

(1) The arms should not be too straight after they are

Fig. 7-13   Fig. 7-14

pushed out, with the elbows down. The pressing of the palms and the shifting of the body weight are harmonious.

(2) There should be no dead corners between the palms and the upper arms. In other words, the palms should not form a right angle with the forearms, but incline slightly forward.

(3) Keep the thumbs apart, and you will find the palms have become warm.

(3) Single Whip

This exercise simulates the use of a whip; that is, striking obliquely down from above or striking forward from behind. In life enhancement, it helps to open the chest and smooth the energy flow, and has the effect of vitalizing one's energy and keeping one fit.

Methods of Practice

Shift the body weight to the left and raise the right tiptoes, turning them inward. Turn the body to the left and move the hands horizontally to the left in a curved shape, palm down, and to the left side of the body. Eyes on the left palm (Fig. 7-15). Inhale slowly while turning the body and moving the palms with the idea that the body and the hips respond to each other and the internal energy swells.

Shift the body weight to the right leg, and turn the body to the right. Move both hands to the right in a curved shape, and place them in front of the right chest, palms to eyebrow level and eyes on the right palm. At the same time, raise the left foot, tiptoes on the ground, and withdraw it a half step to the right (Fig. 7-16). Continue to inhale during the whole process.

Change the right hand into hook, and move the left foot one step to the left, heel first on the ground. Then shift the body weight gradually to the left, and place the whole left foot on the ground. Turn the body to the left,

Fig. 7-15

Fig. 7-16

and at the same time turn the left palm outward in front of the chest and press it forward slowly. Form the Left Bow Step and open the arms, one in front and the other in the rear (Figs. 7-17–18). Eyes look at the left palm. Exhale slowly during the whole process, with the idea that echoes come from all directions, from above and below, and from left and right.

Essential Points

(1) Pivot at the waist for all turning movements in this exercise, and draw an ellipse in the air with both hands.

(2) When in the fixed form of the Single Whip, raise the top of the head up, relax the perineum, and keep the body upright and the frame natural.

(3) Press the left palm forward with the intention of dropping it somewhat.

By practising the Single Whip, you will able to hold the ribs and waist together in twisting the body and carry implicit power. It will produce a magic effect when re-

Fig. 7-17   Fig. 7-18

leased in attacking your opponent. The vital energy flows to Dantian when you press the palm and drop the body, the whole body filling with energy.

(4) Raise Hands and Push Up

In this exercise, first raise the hands and then drop them. Drop them while raising them, and close them while dropping them providing the melody of the inherent movement of cadence.

Methods of Practice

Shift the body weight to the right, left tiptoes inward. Immediately shift the body weight to the right foot, and change the right hand from hook to palm (Fig. 7-19). Keep the left leg firm, raise the right foot, turn the body slightly to the left and swing both arms slightly to the left (Fig. 7-20). Inhale in the above-described process.

Move the right foot one step forward in front of the

Fig. 7-19

Fig. 7-20   Fig. 7-21

left foot, heel on the ground and tiptoes off, and turn the body slightly to the right. At the same time, close the palms in front of the chest, right palm above, fingers to eyebrow level and palm centre toward the left. Left palm is at lower left, with palm facing right and under the right elbow. Eyes look at the fingertips of the right palm (Fig. 7-21). Exhale slowly in the above-described process, with the idea that the hands and feet are integrated, the elbows and knees are integrated, and the shoulders and hips are integrated.

Essential Points

(1) Do not keep the buttocks out in the fixed form. Keep the left armpit empty and relaxed and the right knee slightly bent.

(2) The movements of the hands and feet should be in harmony in the rises and falls, and the head should be slightly up.

(3) In closing the palms, first raise them like a heavy object, and then put them down. Breathe mildly.

In combat, this is a method of preventing the opponent from attacking your chest; that is, use the left hand to press the attacking hand from the opponent, and use the right palm to strike his head and chest.

(5) White Crane Spreads Its Wings

This exercise imitates the perching movements of the white crane. Its beautiful stances and postures provide both closing and opening movements. When the arms are opened, they are spread like the wings of the crane with one foot empty and the other solid.

Methods of Practice

Keep the right foot inward, move the hands downward and to the left in a curved shape, turning the body slightly to the left, eyes on the left palm (Fig. 7-22). Inhale in the above-described process. Shift the body weight to the right leg, raise the left foot and place its tiptoes on the ground in front of the right foot to form the Left Empty Step. At the same time, move the right palm from the right side upward and to the right in a curved shape. When the palm is moved to the upper right, turn the right arm inward so that the palm faces outward, and press the left palm downward past the inside of the bent elbow of the right arm in a curved shape to the left hip (Fig. 7-23). Exhale in the above-described process. Eyes look ahead. In your mind, you are moving like a white crane resting gently and naturally.

Essential Points

(1) Raise the arms simultaneously with the turning of the body. The turning of the arms and the lowering of the body are done in harmony.

(2) Keep the chest in and the back straight with the feeling of extension in the whole body. After practising the exercise for some time, you will find the palm warm and

Fig. 7-22   Fig. 7-23

that the fingers swell.

This exercise is used to parry and block in combat. Use the right hand to parry the attacking hand of the opponent, and use the left hand to guard against the attack from the opponent's leg. Moreover, you can also use your right leg at any time to attack the lower part of his body.

(6) Brush Left Knee with Twist Step

In this exercise, one hand is used to brush the left knee, and the other hand is changed into a pushing palm. The front hand and the front foot are on the opposite side (the left foot and right hand in front). It is therefore called Brush Knee with Twist Step. (When brushing the left knee, it is called the left form; when brushing the right knee, it is called the right form.)

Methods of Practice

Use the waist to turn the body to the right. At the same time move the right palm downward in a curved shape, elbow down and right arm turned outside, so that the palm faces down. Move the left palm upward from below and to the right in a curved shape, eyes on the right palm (Fig. 7-24). Inhale in the above-described process. Continue to turn the body to the right and raise the left foot. Move the right palm to the front of the right chest, and press the left palm downward to the side of the right elbow. Move the left foot forward, land the heel first on the ground and then the whole foot slowly, and shift the body weight to the left leg to form the Left Bow Step. At the same time, brush the left palm downward in a curved shape, and press it to the outer side of the left knee. Push the right palm forward past the ear in a curved shape, and exhale in the process of pushing. You are thinking that you feel steady and full and are pushing the ball in your palm to the infinite distance (Fig. 7-25).

Fig. 7-24   Fig. 7-25

Essential Points

(1) Use the waist to guide the hand movements. The pushing of palms and the shifting of the body weight must be in harmony. Disorder should be avoided in the curved movement of the palms.

(2) In the fixed form, the left fingers point forward and the right fingers point upward. The right elbow is pitted against the left knee. Do not lean the body forward.

(3) The movements should always be curved in pressing and pushing the palms, and straight movements should be avoided.

This exercise helps the arms and legs to extend and flex. The twist step helps to increase the ability to coordinate the movements of all parts of the body. In combat, use the left hand to parry the attack from the opponent and use the right palm to strike the middle and upper parts of the opponent's body.

(7) Play the Pipa

The pipa is a traditional Chinese stringed musical instrument like the lute, but it is held in the arms and played with two hands plucking the strings. In this exercise, the hands are moved with one in front and the other behind as if holding something in a curved shape between them. The hands rise and fall, extend and flex as if playing the pipa, hence the name. In this stance, the left leg is empty while the right leg is solid, implying the idea of advance. In practising this exercise, you should display the artistic conception of free movement.

Methods of Practice

Raise the right foot and move it a half step forward, with the body weight shifted to the right leg. Raise the left foot and land it forward, heel on the ground. At the same time, lift the left palm in a curved shape, turn the left arm outward so that the palm faces to the right, and lower the right palm in a curved shape. Draw the palm back to the left to the inner side of the left elbow, eyes front (Fig.

Fig. 7-26

7-26). Breathe naturally during the whole exercise, with an idea that you are plucking the pipa in your arms, with the whole body moving as an integral whole.

Essential Points

(1) The changing movements of the palms and the change of steps fall in harmony. The distance for the following steps should be kept appropriate to a good degree of balance.

(2) Make sure that the energy reaches all fingers. The internal energy should be lively and flexible. Withdraw the arms, relax the waist and lower the hips. Do the whole exercise in this way, steadily and calmly.

(3) Turn the waist slightly in the whole exercise, first to the right, and then to the left.

(8) Brush Left and Right Knees with Twist Step

This exercise is done symmetrically, and attention should be paid to its continuity.

Methods of Practice

Twist the waist slightly to the right to turn the body to the right, moving the right palm to the right from below, upward in a curved shape. While moving the right arm turn it outward so that the palm faces the upper right. Move the left palm to the right and in front of the right chest and close to the right elbow. Draw the left foot slightly back, tiptoes on the ground. Eyes on the right palm (Fig. 7-27). Exhale mildly while turning the body and moving the palms in the whole process. The following movements are the same as described in Exercise Six in Brush Left Knee with Twist Step (Fig. 7-25).

Shift the body weight backward, raise the left tiptoes, and pivot on the heel, turning outward 45 degrees. Shift the body weight slowly to the left leg, and land the whole left foot on the ground. At the same time, turn the body to the left. While turning the body, move the left palm from below to the upper left in a curved shape. Turn the left arm slightly outward, and move the right palm from front downward to the lower left, and close to the left elbow. Eyes on the left palm. At the same time, raise the right foot, tiptoes on the ground, to form an empty step close to the left foot (Fig. 7-28). Inhale during the whole process.

Move the right foot forward, and land the heel first on the ground and then the whole foot gradually. Shift the body weight to the right leg, and at the same time press the left foot slightly against the ground. Turn the body to the right, and while turning, brush the right palm past the right knee to the right hip in a curved shape. Push the left hand forward slowly from the left ear, eyes front (Fig. 7-29). Exhale slowly in the whole process of turning the body and pushing the palm in an easy manner, not quickly nor slowly.

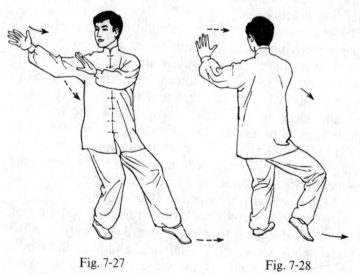

Fig. 7-27

Fig. 7-28

Essential Points

(1) The parts between the thumbs and forefingers of both palms must be fully extended and kept round. In the fixed form, the fingers of the left hand are up and those of the right hand point forward. The body weight should not be shifted forward in pushing the palms.

(2) The sense of touch in pushing the palms is not heavy nor empty. There is nimbleness in the steady movements.

After finishing the Brush Right Knee with Twist Step, do the Brush Left Knee with Twist Step. The movements and essential points are the same as described above (Fig. 7-30).

(9) Parry and Punch with Forward Step

This exercise includes move, parry and punch. The first two are methods for defence, and the last is for attack. When practising this exercise, clear distinction should be made among the three actions. All movements

Fig. 7-29   Fig. 7-30

must be performed in continuity.

Methods of Practice

Shift the body weight backward, left tiptoes outward, and turn the body slightly to the left, left arm outward and palm up. Move the right palm downward to meet the left palm. Eyes on the right palm (Fig. 7-31). Inhale slowly. In the mind, the breath is firmly held.

Shift the body weight gradually to the left leg, and move the right leg forward, heel first on the ground. At the same time, change the right palm into fist and move it from below and inside upward and outward in a curved shape. Move the left palm from below to the upper left and then press it by the right fist, palm centre facing forward right. Eyes look ahead of the right fist (Figs. 7-32 A, B). Exhale mildly in the process of moving the fist. In the mind, the body is kept upright, the fist and palm respond to each other, and yin and yang are integrated.

Shift the body weight slowly to the right leg, place the right foot on the ground, and move the left foot forward, heel on the ground. At the same time, push and press the left palm forward above the right fist, and withdraw the right fist to the waist, fist centre up. Eyes look ahead of the left palm (Fig. 7-33). Inhale mildly while pushing the palm and withdrawing the fist. In the mind, the exercise is open, but not discontinued.

Essential Points

(1) Do not press the armpit too tightly, and do not keep the left elbow too straight. Keep the elbow down. Do not fold the left wrist into a dead corner. Keep the left wrist round and flexible.

(2) Keep the left knee slightly bent.

(3) There should be a curve in the forward step. Do not move the foot straight forward (move the left foot to the front left).

Fig. 7-31

Fig. 7-32A

Fig. 7-32B

Fig. 7-33

(4) The force is on the edge of the left palm. The left arm has a sense of implicit power and is integrated with the back.

Methods of Practice

Shift the body weight forward, keep the whole foot gradually firm on the ground and straighten the right leg slightly to form the Left Bow Step. Hit forward slowly with the right fist, fist eye up. Draw the left palm back to the inner side of the right elbow, palm facing inward and fingers up. Eyes look at the right fist (Fig. 7-34). Exhale slowly in the process of hitting with the fist. In the mind, the manner is imposing and forceful.

Essential Points

(1) Look ahead when hitting with the fist, and integrate the mind, energy and power as if hitting and pushing a giant object to a distant place.

(2) Hitting with the fist and straightening of the right leg are simultaneous so that the power originates from the feet and reaches the fist face.

Fig. 7-34

(10) Apparent Close Up

Apparent Close Up is an exercise for changing the fist into palm and moving the palm. It includes arm turning, palm separating, elbow dropping and push hand. In this exercise, there are varied changes of *Taiji* power, which are used very often in the push hand exercise. The level moving and horizontal parrying with both palms are ward-off methods; that is, they prevent the enemy from attacking the body. Pushing forward with both palms is a closing method; that is, closing the enemy's door, so that the enemy cannot attack, but must stay in a passive position.

Methods of Practice

Part I: Change the right fist gradually into a palm, and at the same time turn the right arm outward. Place the left palm tightly against the right wrist and move it round from the side downward and then forward. At the same time, turn the left arm outward. When both palms are turned up, thrust the left palm to the right forward. At the same time, shift the body weight slightly backward. Eyes look ahead of the right palm (Fig. 7-35).

Straighten the left leg slightly, bend the right knee slightly and continue to shift the body weight backward. At the same time, move the palms flatly and slowly to both sides, palms facing up (Fig. 7-36).

Turn the body slightly to the right, with the shoulders and elbows relaxed and lowered. At the same time, turn both arms inward, and drop both palms down along the central line of the body and press them down with the force on their edges, palms facing obliquely inward. Eyes look between the palms. Use the nose to inhale mildly in the process (Fig. 7-37).

Straighten the right leg a bit, turn the body to the left with the power from the leg. At the same time shift the

Fig. 7-35

Fig. 7-36

Fig. 7-37

Fig. 7-38

body weight forward to form the Left Bow Step. Continue to turn both palms downward and inward and then turn them upward in a curved shape from the abdomen. Press the palms forward slowly with the forward shifting of the body weight, fingers up and palm facing forward. Eyes on the palms, and at the same time exhale mildly (Fig. 7-38).

When withdrawing the palms and turning them inward, gather the natural essence of the air in your mind. When pressing the palms outward, blend the internal and external and make all acupuncture channels work smoothly.

Essential Points

(1) Keep the body firm in practising the exercise. The power for the movement of the hands originates from the feet, and is transmitted to the waist, then to the back, arms and hands. Therefore, keep both feet on the ground in the whole process. Especially in shifting the body weight backward, do not raise the tiptoes, but use the toes to grab the ground.

(2) In pushing the palms forward, the speed should be even, with a sense of resistance. Do not protrude the palms. After the palms are pushed out, the fingers are as high as the shoulders, the elbows slightly down and pitted against the left knee.

(3) The knee of the rear leg is slightly bent.

(4) Keep the body upright instead of leaning it forward. The crown of the head is slightly up.

After practising this exercise for some time, the palms feel as if they are actually pushing a ball in water.

(11) Crossed Hands

In this exercise, the hands are placed across each other like a cross. In the fixed form, the movements are even and symmetrical, but there should be motion in the steady movements.

Methods of Practice

Shift the body weight to the right, left tiptoes raised, and turn the body to the right. Open the palms while turning the body, right palm outside. Move the right palm horizontally to the right in a curved shape. Eyes follow the right palm (Fig. 7-39).

Turn the left foot inward, shift the body weight to the left. Draw the right foot a half step back to the left, tiptoes of both feet forward, standing with feet parallel to form the balance stance. At the same time, move the hands upward from below in a curved shape and cross them in front of the chest, left hand inside and right hand outside, both palms facing inside. Eyes on the palms (Fig. 7-40).

Inhale when turning the body and moving the palms apart, and exhale when crossing the hands. Keep the body upright, hold the vital energy together, and keep the mind empty and abdomen solid.

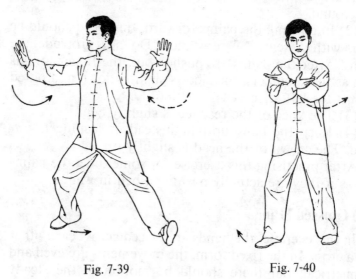

Fig. 7-39   Fig. 7-40

Essential Points

(1) While moving the hands upwad from below, squat slightly, but do not bend the waist.

(2) When the arms circle around, the circle must be round and empty, with the arms fully extended. Relax the crotch and the hips.

(12) Return to Mountains with Tiger in Arms

This exercise starts with the crossed hands in front of the chest. Open them sideways, and push them backward with their directions greatly changed. The "tiger" is used here to mean the opponent; in other words, keep the opponent away from your body. Return to Mountains with Tiger in Arms is one of the principles in practising *Taiji Quan*. Since tigers live in the mountains, the name means returning to the natural surroundings for growth. As a metaphor, you practise the exercise so that your health returns to the pure natural state. In classical Chinese boxing theory, this exercise has the effect of guarding against the enemy in all directions.

Methods of Practice

Part I: Squat slightly, and shift the body weight slowly to the left leg. At the same time, turn the body to the left and raise the right heel lightly, tiptoes on the ground.

While turning the body, move the left arm downward to the left in a curved shape, continuing to move it to the upper left in front of the left ear, palm inside, fingers up and elbow bent. At the same time, move the right palm past the inner side of the left arm and downward to the right. Turn the right arm inward while moving it so that the palm is down and fingers point to the left. Eyes look to the left (Fig. 7-41).

Move the right foot to the forward right. At the same time turn the body slightly to the right. First land the right

121

heel on the ground and then shift the body weight slowly to the right to place the whole foot on the ground. Move the left foot slightly in a turning step to form the Right Bow Step. At the same time, continue to move the right palm downward to the lower right and place it lightly by the right hip. Push the left palm slowly forward while turning the body, palm facing outside and fingers up. Eyes look ahead (Fig. 7-42).

Inhale when turning the body to the left and opening the arms, and exhale when turning to the right and pushing the palm.

Essential Points

(1) The turn of the body in this exercise is 135 degrees (from forward front to rear right). Make sure that the directions are correct. At the beginning, it is easy to err in the directions, but you can adjust by turning the feet properly after landing. However, after you are skillful in the exercise, you will move in the correct direction immediately.

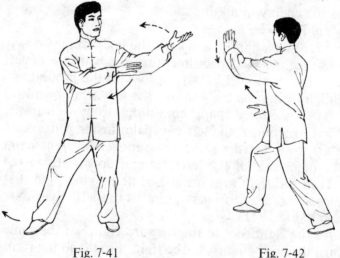

Fig. 7-41   Fig. 7-42

(2) While moving the hands in a curved shape, the eyes follow the movement of the palms and finally look in front of the fingertips of the left hands.

(3) In pushing the left hand, it should pass the ear and then move forward in a curved shape along the central line of the body. While pushing the hand, the arm should be turned slightly inward so that the palm is naturally turned to face forward.

Methods of Practice

Part II: Shift the body weight backward to the left leg, straighten the right leg slightly and turn the body to the left slightly. At the same time, turn the left arm outward until the palm is up, and move it downward in a curved shape to the rear left. Turn the right arm slightly inward until the palm is down, and raise it in a curved shape. The palms are pitted against each other, one above and the other below. The eyes look ahead of the right palm (Fig. 7-43).

Do the downward parry exercise and the press exercise as described in Grasp Peacock's Tail, the only slight difference being the direction (Figs. 7-44–45).

Essential Points

The most salient feature of this exercise is to turn all parts of the body top, bottom, left and right—simultaneously. It therefore calls for a high degree of coordination. All the movements both start and finish simultaneously. The hands should not be kept too widely apart or the body form becomes loose, nor too narrowly apart or the shoulders become tense and the chest pressed. Keep the arms bent.

(13) Punch under Elbow

This is an exercise for using the fist in the Yang-style *Taiji Quan*. In practising this exercise, in which the right

Fig. 7-43

Fig. 7-44

Fig. 7-45

fist is under the elbow, the directions also change from time to time. (This is the most complicated exercise for changes in both direction and footwork.) The footwork includes toe-in step, toe-out step and follow-up step. The beginners should learn this exercise well.

Methods of Practice

Shift the body weight backward and turn the body to the left, right tiptoes raised. While turning the body, move the palms horizontally to the left in a curved shape. Eyes look at the left palm (Fig. 7-46).

Keep the right foot inward and shift the body weight gradually back to the right. At the same time, move the arms to the front of the body, right palm down and left palm up, and move the left foot a half step back, tiptoes on the ground. Eyes on the left palm (Fig. 7-47).

Skip the left foot a half step forward, and follow up with the right foot. Shift the body weight entirely to the right leg, and then move the left foot forward, heel on the ground, to form the left resting stance. While changing the steps, spread out the hands, change the left palm into fist and move it from below to upper right and drop it to the front of the body. Drop the left palm downward from the upper left, and then thrust it upward from the inside of the right elbow. Eyes look ahead of the left palm (Fig. 7-48).

Inhale while turning the body and spreading out the palms, and exhale while thrusting the palm and dropping the fist. In the mind, look right and left, and open and close freely.

Essential Points

(1) While moving the palms horizontally, use the waist to move the shoulders and use the shoulders to move the arms and then the hands. Always keep the elbows bent. There is a feeling that the palms are stroking water.

(2) The range of opening and closing to the left and

Fig. 7-46

Fig. 7-47

Fig. 7-48

right is relatively large. Quickness is the main characteristic in changing the steps. The movements should not be confused. There is opening in the closing movements.

(3) The thrusting of the left palm and the landing of the left heel are completed simultaneously. In thrusting the palm, push the left arm slightly forward.

(4) In the fixed form, the right fist is protected in the left elbow, and the fist is pitted against the left knee. The Baihui acupoint is slightly up, the body upright, the chest turned slightly to the right, and the crotch relaxed.

In combat, this exercise calls for the left hand to be used for defence and the right hand for attack.

(14) Drive Monkeys Back from Left and Right

This is a method for practising the backward steps. Modern scientific research shows that walking backward is good for protecting the cerebrum and also helps to effectively improve the function of the nervous system. The movements in this exercise are light, nimble and natural and involve hand and leg techniques similar to those used by monkeys. In learning this exercise, pay attention to the directions of the hands and feet and unanimity of the movements.

Methods of Practice

Move the left foot slightly inward, tiptoes on the ground. Turn the body slightly to the right, and turn the left arm outward so that the palm is up. At the same time, change the right fist into palm, and move the palm past the abdomen to the upper rear in a curved shape. Turn the right arm outward so that the palm faces up. Eyes on the right palm (Fig. 7-49).

Withdraw the left foot backward, and land the tiptoes first on the ground, and then slowly the whole foot, while shifting the body weight to the left. At the same time, turn the body to the left, moving the left palm back downward in a curved shape, and dropping it in front of the hips, palm up. Push the right palm from the ear. Place the right foot on tiptoes in an empty step. Continue to move the left palm from below to the upper left in the rear, palm up. Turn the right arm outward and so that the palm is up. Eyes on the left palm (Fig. 7-50).

Withdraw the right foot backward, and land the tiptoes first on the ground, and then slowly the whole foot while shifting the body weight to the right. At the same time, turn the body to the right. Move the right palm back downward in a curved shape, and drop it in front of the right hip, palm up, pushing the left palm from the ear. Place the left foot on tiptoes to form an empty step. Eyes on the right palm (Fig. 7-51).

Do the exercise Drive Monkey from Right. Its movements are the same as described in the previous paragraphs.

Inhale while opening the palms, and exhale while withdrawing and pushing the palms. In the mind, the rise is light while the fall is steady.

Essential Points

(1) There should be no clear rises and falls in moving the backward steps. In the mind, however, there can be rises, falls, turns and connections. The body should remain stable and upright.

(2) Do not pause in withdrawing and opening the palms.

In combat, this exercise implies attack in the retreat and guard in the defence. While withdrawing, use the front hand to attack the enemy, and the rear hand to reserve force in preparation for attack.

Fig. 7-49

Fig. 7-50

Fig. 7-51

(15) Oblique Flying

This exercise consists of movements of the hands which spread out like the wings of a bird flying in the air.

Methods of Practice

Shift the body weight gradually and wholly to the left leg, draw the right foot back, and turn the body slightly to the right. At the same time, move the left palm in a curve from below to the left upward, palm facing down. Bend the arm into a semicircle in front of the left chest. Move the right palm from above to the right downward and then to the left to join the left arm as if holding something in between. Eyes on the left palm (Fig. 7-52).

Move the right foot one step forward to the right, heel first on the ground. Then gradually shift the body weight to the right and land the whole foot to form the Right Bow Step. At the same time, move the right palm upward to the upper right behind. In other words, with force on the side of the arm, spread the right arm to the rear right. Move the left palm downward from the inside of the right elbow

Fig. 7-52　　　　　Fig. 7-53

bend, palm down, and press it by the left hip. Eyes on the right palm (Fig. 7-53).

Essential points

(1) The change of direction is wide in this exercise. Attention should be paid to balance.

(2) When flying obliquely, the movements above and below should form a complete whole. The hands and feet should integrate in every movement.

In combat, use the left hand to neutralize the attack and catch the attacking hand of the opponent. Use the right hand with a forward step to hit the opponent's ribs crosswise.

(16) Brush Left Knee with Twist Step

The direction changes 180 degrees from Oblique Flying to Brush Left Knee with Twist Step, and the body weight is shifted from the right leg to the left leg. The relationship between the empty and solid in the changes should be carefully observed.

Methods of Practice

Continue to spread the right arm to the rear right, and follow up with the body to the right side while spreading the arm. Shift the body weight entirely to the right leg, and use the body to move the left arm to rub to the right in a curved shape.

Move the right heel slightly outward so that the tiptoes point to the forward left. At the same time, turn the body slightly to the left. Turn the right arm inward first and move it to the upper right in a curved shape. Then turn it outward and raise it to the upper right, palm up. At the same time, move and turn the left palm from the lower left to the upper right and then to the lower right in a curved shape. Press it in front of the right elbow, palm down, eyes on the right palm. Draw the left foot half a step back to the right foot, heel off and tiptoes on the ground to form the Left Empty Step (Fig. 7-54).

Move the left foot one step forward to the left, heel on the ground. Move the left palm to the lower left in a curved shape, and push the right palm from the right ear side forward to the left. Turn the body to the left while pushing the palms, the same as described in the previous Brush Left Knee with Twist Step. The direction is forward left (Fig. 7-55).

Essential Points

(1) The process of turning the right arm inward and outward with the curved movement of the right palm and the process of moving the left palm from left to right are identical. The eyes follow the movement of the right palm.

(2) Keep the left arm two palms away from the chest. Keep the left wrist relaxed and flat.

(3) The turns to the right and to the left should be clear and not too mechanical, but continuous and natural. There is no clear break at the turns. When you are skillful

Fig. 7-54   Fig. 7-55

in the exercise, you will find the trend of the following movement implied in the preceding movement. This embodies the characteristics of *Taiji Quan*—all the exercises and movements are continuously connected.

(17) Needle at Sea Bottom

In this exercise, you bend the body forward with the palm fingers downward as if getting something precious from the bottom of the sea. The "needle" here refers to the fingers, implying their downward thrust.

Methods of Practice

Shift the body weight entirely to the left leg, raise the right foot and move it a half step forward. When the right foot leaves the ground, raise the heel first, and then the tiptoes. In landing the foot, land the tiptoes first and then gradually the whole sole. Shift the body weight to the right leg, at the same time moving the body slightly backward. Semultaneously, turn about 45 degrees to the right side. Raise the left foot, and draw it a half step back, tiptoes on the ground, to form the Left Empty Step.

Drop the right palm in a curved shape while turning the body with a retreating step. Turn the right arm slightly while dropping the palm so that the palm faces inside. At the same time, move the left palm in a curved shape to the upper left, and turn the left arm outward slightly so that the palm faces obliquely outside and slightly above the left shoulder. Eyes look at the rear right (Fig. 7-56). Keep the left elbow slightly down and the right palm about two fists from the body. Keep the body upright. Use the nose to inhale naturally in the above-described process.

Move the left tiptoes slightly forward to such a degree that you feel comfortable and stable. At the same time, continue to move the right arm in a semicircle upward to the right, and turn the right arm outward so that the palm

133

faces up. Bend the right elbow, move the right palm past the side of the ear in a curved shape downward and forward below, planting it in front of the left tiptoes. Move the left palm from above past the chest in a curved shape to the lower left to grab downward, palm down, and press it by the left hip. Eyes on the right palm. Exhale lightly. See Figs. 7-57A, B for side and front views. In the mind, penetrate into the ground.

Essential Points

(1) In the fixed form, the right elbow is pitted against the left knee, and the right hand against the left foot. Keep the left arm bent inside, fingers to the forward right. Keep the chest slightly in, and keep the right elbow properly bent.

(2) In practising this exercise, the back should not be bent, hips not too tight, the head not down, and the buttocks not out.

(3) Keep the fingers of the planting palm naturally apart.

(4) Keep the left knee properly bent. This is good for balance. If it is too straight, you will find a sense of tension in the abdomen and it is not good for the circulation of the blood throughout the body.

(5) Do not shrug the shoulder in the process of drawing a vertical circle with the right palm.

(6) Place the feet on both sides of the central line of the body. This is good for keeping the body stable.

(7) While planting the palm downward, lower the body weight slightly.

In combat, this exercise is of great value. It uses the left hand to parry the attack from the opponent. When you bend your body, use the right fingers to hit the lower parts of the opponent's body, such as the legs, feet and crotch. As far as life enhancement is concerned, the movements

Fig. 7-56

Fig. 7-57A   Fig. 7-57B

effectively improve the functions of the lower limbs, increase the elasticity of the muscles, and postpone the aging of the muscles.

(18) Flash the Arms

In this exercise, the arms are raised so as to straighten the back and increase the waist power. In this way the whole body, from feet to hands, are closely connected with the back and shoulders during the transition into one integral whole.

Methods of Practice

Raise the arms up slowly, and in the course of the raising, put the left hand lightly on the right wrist. The left palm faces the right, and the right palm faces the left. At the same time, raise the upper part of the body slowly and keep it erect, left tiptoes slightly touching the ground to increase the power. The crown of the head is slightly up so that the top and the bottom respond to each other. Eyes on the right palm (Fig. 7-58).

Move the left foot one step forward, heel first on the ground and then gradually the whole foot. Shift the body weight forward at the same time and straighten the rear leg slightly to form the Left Bow Step. At the same time, turn the right arm inward so that the palm is up, and gradually pull it to the rear right, back of the hand obliquely against the right temple. Turn the left palm inward so that the palm faces forward, and push it forward slowly, keeping the palm to shoulder level, thumb wide apart. Eyes look ahead (Fig. 7-59).

Inhale while raising the body and closing the palms, and exhale while holding up the palms, with the idea that the two palms are holding up the sky.

Essential Points

(1) In the fixed form, keep the head upright, lower

Fig. 7-58   Fig. 7-59

chin in, and both arms bent. The upper part of the body faces the front, but slightly to the right. Avoid shrugging the shoulders. The palms above are pitted against each other, both cupped.

(2) Pull the palms apart, in conformity with the forward shift of the body weight. The left elbow and left knee form a vertical line while the left palm and left foot also form a vertical line.

(3) The fingers of the left hand are up while the right fingers are obliquely up, making this exercise look both open and implicit.

(4) When raising the upper part of the body, if you find the left foot not in a proper place (too forward for the body to rise), move the left foot slightly backward, the tiptoes on the ground.

In combat, this exercise uses the right hand to catch the opponent's wrist and pull it to the side rear so that the opponent loses his balance. At the same time, it uses the left palm to strike the opponent's chest or to seize him by the throat. In life enhancement, the exercise helps to carry the vital energy to all fingers and make the acupuncture channels work smoothly.

(19) Turn Around and Punch

Turn Around and Punch is another boxing exercise in the Yang-style *Taiji Quan*. Turn around refers to the direction change of the body by twisting the waist and turning backward. Punch refers to the throwing of the fist from inside to outside while turning the body. In this exercise, the left hand is empty, and the right fist is solid. The left leg is supplementary and the right leg plays the main role.

Methods of Practice

Sit backward, and shift the body weight to the right leg. At the same time, raise the left tiptoes slowly and turn them to the inner side.

Pivot on the left foot and twist the body to the right. At the same time, change the right palm into a fist and move it down to the front of the abdomen along the central line of the body while turning the body. Move the left hand horizontally to the right while turning the body to protect the left forehead from upper left, left palm pitted obliquely against the right fist. Eyes look at the rear right. The right armpit should be relaxed and loose, and the crotch round (Fig. 7-60).

Land the whole left foot on the ground, and shift the body weight to the left leg. Raise the right foot and draw it back, immediately moving the tiptoes out. Land the foot to the right backward with the heel. At the same time, continue to turn the body to the right, back of the right hand facing forward. Throw it from inside to outside, and from left to right, and land it in front of the body. Move the left palm down from above in a curved shape, and press the palm downward in front of the left part of the waist. Eyes look ahead (Fig. 7-61).

Inhale while turning the right palm into fist and dropping it down, and exhale while throwing the fist. The mind is concentrated between the fist and the palm, and the energy stream flows to Dantian.

Essential Points

(1) In the fixed form, the neck should be erect, the central line of the body falls between the feet. The right fist is in front, and is pitted against the right foot. The right elbow is slightly bent and is pitted against the right knee. The left palm is pitted obliquely against the right elbow, and the left arm is bent inward and circles around the abdomen. Raise the right tiptoes, but do not stick them up intentionally, buttocks sitting slightly backward and forming a vertical line with the heel of the rear foot. Keep the right fist to the right shoulder level, palm obliquely up. Do not clench the fist too tightly.

Fig. 7-60

Fig. 7-61

(2) Throwing the fist, moving the right foot forward and turning the body are all performed in coordination. When the foot lands on the ground, the fist is thrown out.

(3) In twisting and turning the body, do not incline the backbone.

(4) After moving the right foot forward, keep the right knee slightly bent.

(5) The feet should be kept properly apart, or the movements will be too small for proper execution. If the movements are too large, they will cause clear rises and falls in the body weight.

This exercise helps to improve the agility of the waist and the coordination between the hands.

In combat, dodge and use the left hand to seal off the attacking fist and palm from the opponent, and immediately throw the fist to hit the opponent's face.

(20) White Snake Thrusts Out Tongue

To imitate animals' movements is one of the ideas for life enhancement in *Taiji Quan*. It is through the imitation of the habits of animals that helps us to strengthen our muscles and bones and to vitalize our energy. In this exercise, the palms are interlocked with each other or stretched out in the shape of a snake thrusting out its tongue, and the arms are moved like a snake crawling. In practising this exercise, lean the body slightly forward. However, the force originates from the back, so it is necessary to keep the back perfectly round.

Methods of Practice

Raise the right foot and move it slightly forward, heel first on the ground. Straighten the rear leg slightly and shift the body weight gradually forward so that the whole foot becomes firm on the ground. Change the right fist into palm and pull it back slowly in a curved shape, placing it in front of the right side of the waist, palm up, as if holding something on the palm. Move the left palm from below and push it upward and forward in a curved shape, palm facing forward, fingers up. Eyes look in front of the left palm (Fig. 7-62).

Breathe naturally in the whole exercise. The mind follows the pushing hand to the remote front.

Essential Points

(1) The left wrist forms an obtuse angle exceeding 90 degrees. Avoid right angles. The left palm is as high as the left shoulder and the right elbow slightly bent. Keep it empty under the left armpit.

(2) Withdraw the fist, push the palm and shift the body weight all should be done harmoniously.

(3) Push the left palm over the right palm. In the fixed form, the right palm and the left elbow correspond to each other.

(4) The left palm is located at the central line of the body. Do not incline it to either side.

Fig. 7-62

(5) Bend the right arm into an arc, palm about two fists away from the waist.

In combat, uses the right hand to stop the opponent's attacking foot, and uses the left palm to hit his chest. At the same time, keep the right palm ready for attack.

(21) Oblique Flying

Methods of Practice

Shift the body weight backward, raise the right tiptoes and keep them outward. Turn the body slightly to the right. At the same time, move the right palm from below upward to the right, turn it to face down and place it in front of the right chest. Move the left palm from above downward to the left and then close it to the right, palm up to face the right palm. Eyes on the right palm (Fig. 7-63).

Shift the body weight gradually to the right leg and keep the right foot firm on the ground. Raise the left foot and move it forward to the left, heel first on the ground.

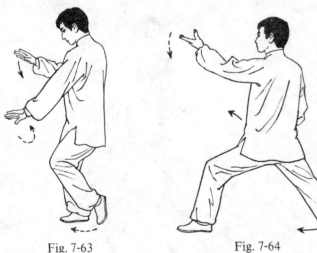

Fig. 7-63   Fig. 7-64

Gradually shift the body weight to the left leg and keep the left foot firm on the ground to form the Left Bow Step. Move the hands in the same way as described in Exercise Fifteen (Fig. 7-64).

Inhale while closing the arms, and exhale while flying out.

The essential points are the same as described in Exercise Fifteen in Oblique Flying.

(22) Grasp Peacock's Tail

Methods of Practice

Shift the body weight to the right, keep the right leg firm, and raise the left tiptoes. Pivot on the left heel, turn the body to the left and keep the left foot firmly on the ground. Shift the body weight gradually to the left leg, raise the right leg and rest it by the left foot, tiptoes on the ground. At the same time, turn the left arm inward and move it horizontally to the front of the left chest. Move the right palm past the chest to the left in a curved shape to close with the left palm in an embrace (Fig. 7-65). Eyes look at the rear left.

Essential Points

(1) Shift the body weight to the left leg simultaneously with the raising of the right foot. Keep balance. Do not sway the body.

(2) The left arm is bent in an arc, lower than the left shoulder.

(3) Shift to the left with the right palm in harmony with the turning of the body. Do not move the arm by itself.

Subsequent movements, as well as the essential points, are the same as described in Exercise Two in Grasp Peacock's Tail (Fig. 7-66).

143

Fig. 7-65   Fig. 7-66

(23) Single Whip

The moves which connect the preceding exercise Grasp Peacock's Tail to Single Whip are the same as described in Exercise Two and Exercise Three (Fig. 7-67).

(24) Wave Hands Like Clouds

Wave Hands Like Clouds is one of the most typical exercises in Yang-style *Taiji Quan*. Moreover, there is a big difference in this exercise between the Yang-style and the Chen-style. In practising this exercise, move the hands alternately in front of the body. The movements include turning the hands inward and outward, with rises and falls of the palms. Move feet with the waist and sway the body lightly like walking in the air and waving hands like clouds. Lightness, nimbleness and smoothness are among the most salient features of the exercise. Movement of the waist, side walk and palm turning are the three key movements for doing the exercise well.

144

Fig. 7-67

Methods of Practice

Shift the body weight slightly to the right, and keep the left foot inward and firm. Turn the body slightly to the right and change the right hook hand into palm. Turn the palm upside down while turning the body and move it to the right. At the same time, move the left palm from left downward and then to the right in a curved shape, palm facing inside, and then to the right elbow (Fig. 7-68). Eyes on the right palm.

Shift the body weight to the left, and immediately turn the body to the left. Raise the right leg, move it a half step closer to the left foot, and land it, tiptoes on the ground. Move the left palm from below upward and to the left, and move the right palm from above downward to the left. Eyes follow the movement of the hands (Fig. 7-69).

Keep the right foot firmly on the ground, shift the body weight to the right, and move the left foot a half

Fig. 7-68

Fig. 7-69

Fig. 7-70

step crosswise to the left, tiptoes first on the ground. At the same time, turn the body to the right, and move the arms in a curved shape while turning the body, right palm upward and to the right, and left palm downward and to the right. Immediately shift the body weight to the left, keep the left foot firm on the ground and raise the right foot, moving it horizontally to the left (Fig. 7-70). Land the tiptoes first on the ground and then gradually the whole right foot. Shift the body weight to the right leg, and move the left foot to the left. At the same time, move the left hand from below upward and to the left, and the right hand from above to the lower right and to the left in a curved shape. In this way, move the feet and arms alternately, and repeat three times.

Breathe naturally in the whole exercise. In the mind, move like a breeze stroking the sleeves, round and naturally.

Essential Points

(1) When moving the arms alternately, always keep the left palm pitted against the right elbow, and the right palm against the left elbow.

(2) When moving the left foot horizontally, the starting step should not be too big or the body will incline.

(3) When following up with the right foot, avoid grabbing the ground with the tiptoes. Raise and land them both lightly.

(4) Move the hands with the body like a complete entity. In turning the body, pivot at the waist. Keep the backbone upright at the beginning.

This exercise helps to invigorate the waist, back, shoulders and arms. In combat, move the hands continuously in tight defence to make it difficult for the enemy to attack you.

(25) Single Whip

Methods of Practice

After repeating the exercise Wave Hands Like Clouds three times, shift the body weight to the right leg and change the right palm into hook by the right side of the body. Move the left foot to the left and shift the body weight to the left to form the Left Bow Step. While turning the body to the left, press the left palm forward, palm facing obliquely forward (Fig. 7-71).

The essential points are the same as described in the previous Single Whip exercises.

(26) Pat High on Horse

One step empty on the ground, and one step backward. One hand in front and one hand in rear. The exercise looks as if you are mounting a horse with the reins in hand.

Methods of Practice

Shift the body weight forward, and move the right leg a half step forward. Then shift the body weight to the right leg, raise the left leg and move it forward, tiptoes on the ground to form an empty step. At the same time, change the right hand from hook to palm, bend the elbow and push it forward from the side of the ear, palm facing down and fingers pointing obliquely forward left. Turn the left arm outward, palm facing up, bend the arm and draw the palm back near to the body. Eyes look ahead (Fig. 7-72).

Inhale when bending the arm with a forward right step, and exhale when landing the left step and pushing the palm. In the mind, hold the *Taiji* in your arms.

Essential Points

(1) When changing the hand from hook to palm, the transition should be natural and round. First open the thumb, and then the other fingers. Turn the right arm

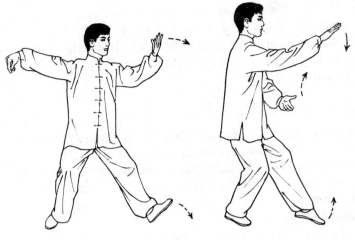

Fig. 7-71   Fig. 7-72

outward immediately, and open fingers so that the palm faces up. In this process, extend the right arm slightly out and twist the body slightly to the right. Look back at the right hand, bend the elbow and push the palm forward.

(2) Bending the elbow and pushing the palm should be identical with the right step forward. When the palm is pushed to the side of the ear, touch the right tiptoes to the ground.

(3) In shifting the body weight between the legs, the movement should be light. Keep the body from rising and falling.

(4) The right arm should not be pushed out too far, right elbow slightly down, and left elbow bent.

(5) The right palm should not be higher than eye level.

(6) Do not press the left armpit too tightly. Keep the armpit loose, and the left palm about two fists from the abdomen.

(7) Keep both palms in.

149

In combat, the exercise is a method for defence with hidden attack. When the enemy tries to seize your left wrist, just withdraw the left hand and attack the enemy with the right palm, and at the same time step forward to kick with the right foot.

(27) Kick Out with Right Foot

This exercise is an important leg technique used in Yang-style *Taiji Quan*. In practising, rise and fall slowly, calmly and steadily. As only one leg is used to support the body, and the body is fully spread out, particular attention should be paid to balance. Do not sway the body.

Methods of Practice

Turn the body slightly to the right, raise the left foot and move it forward to the left, heel first on the ground. At the same time, move the right palm from front to the right and then inward in a curved shape. Move the left palm to the left, forward and then to the right in a curved shape. Eyes on the left palm (Fig. 7-73).

Fig. 7-73

Shift the body weight to the left to form the Left Bow Step. Move the right palm forward over the left arm bend. Move the left palm in a curved form from under the right arm in front of the right chest, and pit it against the right elbow. Eyes on the right palm (Fig. 7-74).

Shift the body weight to the left, move the right foot forward with a follow-up step, turning the body to the left. While turning the body, move the palms to the left for the downward parry. Eyes on the left (Fig. 7-75).

Bend the right leg and raise it, and cross the hands in front of the chest (Fig. 7-76).

Kick forward to the right with the right foot, instep flat, move the palms apart to both sides and push them outward. Eyes look forward to the right (Fig. 7-77).

Inhale when raising the knee and crossing arms, exhale when kicking with the right foot and pushing the palms. In the mind, the energy reaches all parts of the body, and all movements are balanced.

Essential Points

(1) In the fixed form, bend the left knee slightly to keep balance. Do not straighten the right knee entirely. Keep the joints nimble. Pit the right elbow against the right knee. All fingers and the right foot feel infinitely extended. The left toes grab the ground lightly. The Baihui at the crown of the head is slightly up.

(2) The arms are straight, but slightly bent. Both elbows are arched and both wrists are at shoulder level.

(3) In moving, the left palm closes from outside to inside while the right palm closes from inside to outside, as if the hands are linked by something between them. Turn the waist and hips to the left and right while moving, and move the feet accordingly. As a result, there are three levels of circles—above (hands), middle (waist) and below (feet).

| Fig. 7-74 | Fig. 7-75 |

| Fig. 7-76 | Fig. 7-77 |

(4) In the process of changing from Fig. 7-74 to Fig. 7-75, because the left hand moves along a very long line, its speed of movement should be quicker than that of the right hand so that both hands reach the designated positions at the same time.

(5) When raising the knee and crossing the hands, the movements should be slow, left hand inside and right hand outside. In the mind, the whole essence of the air under the sky is held in the embrace. The hands are crossed at wrist, not too close to the chest. Do not shrug the shoulders. In crossing the hands, turn the body slightly to the right, and the eyes look between the palms.

(6) Moving and turning the body are identical, while moving the hands apart and kicking are also identical.

(28) Strike Opponent's Ears with Both Fists

This exercise is a method of using the fists to strike the centre from both sides, with the ears of the enemy as the target for attack. The bow step is used in this exercise to increase the fist power to train the total force in striking with both fists at the same time.

Methods of Practice

Withdraw the right leg, turn the body slightly to the right, move the arms outward, and withdraw them in a curved shape to the two sides of the right knee (Fig. 7-78).

Land the right foot forward, heel first on the ground, and gradually shift the body weight to the right, the whole right foot on the ground, to form the Right Bow Step. At the same time, change the palms into fists and thrust them out in a curved shape from both sides, fist eye to fist eye, and at ear level. Eyes look forward and up. (Fig. 7-79).

Inhale when withdrawing the right leg and the palms, exhale when thrusting the fists out. In your mind, the two fists are integrated.

153

Fig. 7-78   Fig. 7-79

Essential Points

(1) When withdrawing the leg, turn the body steadily in a small angle to the right by pivoting on the left heel with no ups and downs. When withdrawing the palms, move the turning arms to draw circles in the air. Close the arms first, and then draw them back to the sides of the waist, all fingers forward.

(2) When drawing the right leg back, keep the right tiptoes down and the thigh level.

(3) When thrusting the fists, press the left foot slightly against the ground to provide power to the fists, forming a straight line with the waist and fists.

(4) When thrusting the fists, do not shrug the shoulders, nor straighten the back. Relax the hips.

(5) Keep the arms bent into a circle.

(6) Keep the body upright. Do not bend the body nor the head.

(7) Do not clench the fists too tightly. Shifting the

154

body weight forward and propelling the fists should be one simultaneous movement.

(29) Kick Out with Left Foot

All movement are symmetrical to the exercise Kick Out with Right Foot.

Methods of Practice

Shift the body weight slightly backward, and keep the right foot slightly outward and firm on the ground. Move the left foot forward, change the fists into palms and move them upward from below in a curved shape. (Fig. 7-80).

Bend the left leg and raise it, crossing the arms in front of the body (Fig. 7-81).

Kick forward to the left with the left foot, instep flat. Move the palms apart and push them outward at the same time. Eyes look ahead of the left palm (Fig. 7-82).

The essential points for the exercise are the same as described for the exercise Kick Out with Right Foot.

(30) Right Heel Kick with Body Turn

The leg technique used in this exercise is similar to that for the Kick Out With Right Left Foot. The only difference is the force point on the heel. In the process of changing the postures, the turning range of the body is fairly large, and the direction should be correct.

Methods of Practice

Raise the right heel slightly and twist and turn the body quickly to the right backward. While turning, move the left foot downward and land it by the right foot, tiptoes first on the ground. Shift the body weight gradually to the left, keep the left foot firm on the ground, bend the right leg and raise it. At the same time, move the arms downward from above while turning the body, and cross

Fig. 7-80

Fig. 7-81   Fig. 7-82

them in front of the chest, right arm outside and left arm inside (Fig. 7-83).

Kick forward to the right with the right foot, force on the heel, and tiptoes up. Keep the leg at hip level. At the same time, move the palms apart, palms facing outside, and push the palms outward in a curved shape. Eyes front right (Fig. 7-84).

Inhale when turning the body, raising the knee and crossing hands, and exhale when kicking. In the mind, open all the acupuncture channels in the body, and breathe to the depth of the internal organs.

Essential Points

(1) When turning the body to the right backward, pivot on the right sole, heel slightly raised. The movement of turning the body in this way is more nimble. The angle for the turn is 180 degrees.

(2) The body turn should be light and stable. It can be a bit quicker than usual, but not too quick. Keep the body upright in the process of turning the body.

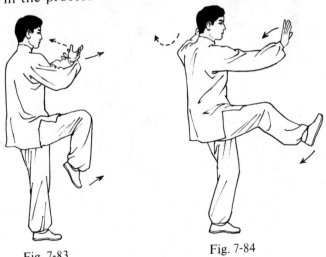

Fig. 7-83   Fig. 7-84

(3) The arms can be opened slightly wider in coordination with the body turn, but keep the elbows bent.

(31) Beat Tiger from Left

Beat Tiger is executed in two exercises—left and right —in the Yang-style *Taiji Quan*. The fists are placed as if beating a tiger. It is a common posture used by warriors in ancient China, described as, "not an action in reality." The movements of the tiger beaters drawn in ancient Chinese paintings are similar.

Methods of Practice

Land the right foot by the left foot, tiptoes first on the ground, and gradually shift the body weight to the right leg. Raise the left foot and move it backward to the left, gradually shifting the body weight to the left to form the Left Bow Step. At the same time, move the palms to the right and downward in a curved shape, and clench the right fist, placing it by the left ribs, fist eye up. Eyes look

Fig. 7-85

forward right (Fig. 7-85).

The exercise helps to increase the strength of the whole body and strengthen the waist and back.

Essential Points

(1) In the fixed form, the left arm is bent inward and the right arm is bent around the chest. Do not shrug the left shoulder. Keep the waist and hips down. The right fist is pitted against the left elbow. Keep the wrists relaxed and flat.

(2) When withdrawing the right foot, land the heel first on the ground, and then slowly the whole foot. In changing the palms into fists, press the right foot slightly against the ground.

(3) Raising the left arm up and bending the right arm around the chest should be well coordinated.

(4) As the line of movement for the left hand is longer than that for the right hand, the movement should be quick so as to ensure that both hands reach the designated position at the same time.

(5) When moving the palms, the arms should be round, the steps light and quick. After landing the foot firmly, shift the body weight slowly.

(32) Beat Tiger from Right

Methods of Practice

Keep the left foot inward and firm on the ground, turn the body to the right, raise the right foot and land it on the ground to the right backward. Shift the body weight gradually to the right to form the Right Bow Step. While turning the body and changing steps, change the fists into palms and move them downward in a curved shape and to the upper right. Change the right palm into fist again and place it over the head to the upper right. Change the left palm into fist and place it horizontally under the right ribs. Eyes front left (Figs. 7-86 A, B).

Breathe naturally throughout the exercise. In the mind, tame the dragon and the tiger with calmness.

The essential points for the exercise are the same as described for the exercise Beat Tiger from Left.

When changing from the left exercise to the right exercise, the direction changes. At this time, move the feet slightly so as to suit the turn of the body.

(33) Part Wild Horse's Mane

In this exercise, the arms are so opened as if the mane on a horse's head is parted on two sides. The moving stance in parting the arms resembles a galloping horse.

Methods of Practice

Shift the body weight to the left, right tiptoes raised, and pivot on the heel to turn the body to the right. At the same time, change the fists into palms, and move the right palm downward, right and upward again, and the left palm upward, forward and to the right again in a curved shape

Fig. 7-86A   Fig. 7-86B

to close (Fig. 7-87).

Keep the right foot firmly on the ground, shift the body weight to the right leg, and draw the left foot slightly back, tiptoes touching the ground. At the same time, embrace with the arms, right palm facing down, and left palm facing up. Eyes on the left palm (Fig. 7-88).

Move the left foot one step to the left, heel first on the ground. Gradually shift the body weight and keep the left foot firmly on the ground to form the Left Bow Step. While shifting the body weight, part the hands, move the left palm, thumb outside, to the upper left in a curved shape at eyebrow level, and press the right palm in a curved shape to the right downward by the right hip. Eyes follow the movement of the left palm. In the fixed form, the eyes look forward to the left (Fig. 7-89).

Inhale when shifting the body weight and closing the arms, and exhale when parting the palms. In the mind, do the exercise freely and with a mighty force.

Essential Points

(1) When changing the fists into palms, the right hand draws a vertical circle counter clockwise by the right side of the body while the left hand draws a vertical circle by the left side of the body. Immediately after that, the hands are closed on the right. After they are parted, they are closed again.

(2) When the hands are holding a ball by the right side of the body, the upper hand is not higher than shoulder level, elbow slightly down, while the lower hand is at waist level. Keep the wrists relaxed and flat. Eyes look between the palms.

(3) When closing the arms, the left palm should be pitted against the right elbow so that the arms are in proper relationship.

(4) When parting the palms and shifting the body

161

Fig. 7-87

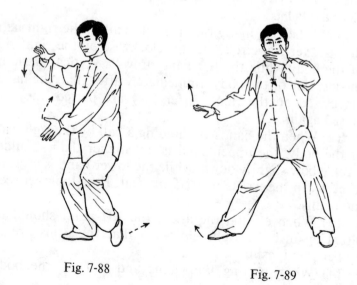

Fig. 7-88

Fig. 7-89

weight, there is a natural movement of turning the body to the left, and this should be done as a complete whole.

(5) When the arms are spread out, energy reaches all parts of the body from heel to finger.

This exercise is a method of advancing to attack the enemy, by which the rear hand is used to seize the enemy by the wrist, and the front hand is thrust out from under his armpit to knock him down.

(34) Jade Girl Works at Shuttles

This exercise involves varied hand techniques, by which the hands move to and fro like shuttles, similar to a woman working at a loom in ancient China, hence the name. The metaphor describes the movements in this exercise as lithe and graceful.

Methods of Practice

Shift the body weight to the right, raise the left tiptoes and keep them inward, turning the body to the right. At the same time, turn the left arm inward, move the left palm downward and to the right in a curved shape, palm facing obliquely inside. Raise the right arm up in a curved shape, palm facing down, and eyes looking to the right backward (Fig. 7-90). Keep the whole left foot firmly on the ground, shift the body weight to the left leg, bend the right leg, raise it, move it to the right and land it backward to the right, heel first on the ground. While moving the right leg, turn the body to the right, and move the palms naturally for an embrace in front of the right chest, right palm facing down, and left palm facing up. Eyes on the right palm (Fig. 7-91).

Keep the whole right foot firmly on the ground, shifting the body weight to the right leg. Bend the left leg, raise it, and land it forward to the left, heel first on the ground. Then gradually shift the body weight to the left, and

163

Fig. 7-90

Fig. 7-91

Fig. 7-92

Fig. 7-93

straighten the right leg to form the Left Bow Step. At the same time, move the left arm in a curved shape to the upper left for an upward parry. While blocking, turn the arm inward so that the palm faces outside. Move the right palm upward from below in a curved shape and press it forward to the left. Eyes look ahead (Figs. 7-92–93).

Shift the body weight backward and turn the body slightly to the right. At the same time, move both palms in a curved shape to rub horizontally to the lower left, palm facing down (Fig. 7-94). Shift the body weight to the left, turn the body to the left, and at the same time raise the right foot, tiptoes touching the ground. At the same time, move the left palm naturally to the left while turning the body and turn the right palm over to face up and move it in front of the left chest. Eyes look at the lower left (Fig. 7-95).

Bend the right foot, raise it and land it forward to the right, heel first on the ground. Turn the body to the right, shift the body weight to the right, and keep the whole right foot firmly on the ground to form the Right Bow Step. At the same time, move the right arm in a curved shape to the upper right for an upward parry. While blocking, turn the arm inward so that the palm faces outside. Move the left palm upward from below in a curved shape and press it forward to the right. Eyes look ahead (Fig. 7-96).

This exercise is done twice, once on the left side and once on the right side. Inhale when embracing, and exhale when blocking in each exercise. This exercise, interchangeable between the left and the right, helps to invigorate the blood circulation of the entire body. In the mind, the movements are lithe, nimble and lively.

Essential Points

(1) After the arms are thrust out, keep them in curved shape, thumb to thumb, fingers of the upper hand point-

Fig. 7-94

Fig. 7-95

Fig. 7-96

Fig. 7-97

ing obliquely up and those of the lower hand pointing down.

(2) The upper palm is obliquely above the head, back of the hand facing the forehead.

(3) Keep the body from rising and falling while changing steps, turning the body and shifting the body weight. Do not shrug while blocking with the palms.

(4) In executing the palm block movements, turn the body at a 90-degree angle. The left and right movements are symmetrical.

(35) Push Down

Push Down is an exercise in the Yang-style *Taiji Quan* in which the body weight rises and falls clearly. Its stance is the crouch stance. The exercise mainly improves the function of the legs and effectively increases the flexibility of the body techniques.

Methods of Practice

Raise the left tiptoes, pivot on the heel and move the left foot outward. At the same time, gradually shift the body weight to the left leg and turn the body to the left while shifting the weight. Move the left hand in a curved shape downward and past the abdomen and raise it to the upper left of the body. While raising the hand, change the palm into hook with the five fingers clenched together. At the same time, move the right hand past the head in a curved shape to the left. While moving, turn the right arm so that the palm faces inside, and place the right palm to the oblique front of the left elbow. By this time, the left hook is slightly higher than the left shoulder. Simultaneously with the movement of the palm, bend the left leg and squat with the right leg lowered (Fig. 7-97). Eyes on the left hook.

167

Twist the waist and turn the body to the right. At the same time, turn the right arm outward, and turn the right palm over to face outside, fingers pointing forward. Thrust them forward in a curved shape along the inner side of the right leg. Eyes on the right palm. By this time, the body weight is lowered to a proper height in coordination with the crouch stance and palm thrusting (Fig. 7-98).

Inhale when changing direction and shifting the body weight, and exhale when thrusting the palm with the crouch stance. In the mind, the palm and hook are integrated.

Essential Points

(1) The body weight should change slowly and roundly. It should not be lowered suddenly to undermine the style of the integral whole of the *Taiji Quan*.

(2) While turning the body to the left, turn the right foot slightly. But in the fixed form with the crouch stance, turn the right tiptoes naturally to the forward right.

(3) Do not protrude the buttocks, nor bend the head

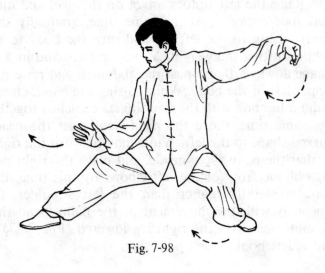

Fig. 7-98

and the body too much.

(4) The degree of squat in the crouch stance depends on the physique of the practitioner. The crouch stance can be higher for those not in good health.

(36) Golden Cock Stands on One Leg

In this exercise, the practitioner stands on one leg like a cock, with the hands opened like a cock's plumes. In practising the exercise, you find yourself tall, straight and forceful.

Methods of Practice

Press the left leg against the ground so that the body weight is shifted forward. Stand erect with the right leg for support, bend the left leg and raise it. At the same time, change the left hook into palm, move it forward from behind and snap it upward from below, fingers up, and left elbow against the left knee. When snappping the left palm upward, move the right palm in a curved shape and press it by the right hip. Eyes look ahead (Fig. 7-99).

Drop the left foot lightly and land it by the inner side of the right foot. At the same time, bend the right leg and raise it. While doing all this, drop the left palm lightly and press it by the left hip, snapping the right palm upward from below. Eyes look ahead (Fig. 7-100).

Breathe naturally throughout the exercise. In the mind, keep the body firm and upright, with all movements well-connected and executed.

Essential Points

(1) In the process of shifting the body weight from the left leg to the right leg, the left hook is immediately changed into palm and is pressed slightly backward so as to help shift the weight. When raising the left leg, raise the heel first, tiptoes on the ground. After the right leg is firm on the floor, raise the whole foot.

Fig. 7-99   Fig. 7-100

(2) The thrusting up of one hand and the dropping of the other should be well-coordinated.

(3) The tiptoes of the raised foot should be down and relaxed. Relax the hips.

(4) Keep the elbow of the upper arm relaxed, bent and down, and the fingers of the lower palm pointing obliquely forward.

(5) The change between the rise and fall of the legs should be natural and continuous. Avoid any sense of leaping.

(6) Keep balance in practising the exercise. Keep the supporting leg slilghtly bent to increase its firmness and stability.

(7) The process of changing from Push Down to Cock Stands on One Leg should be slow and gradual.

(8) When dropping the left leg, land the tiptoes first on the ground and then the whole foot.

In combat, the upper hand is used to snap and hit the

enemy's chest and head. The knee is raised to hit the crotch and abdomen.

(37) Strike Down with Forward Step

This is another exercise in the Yang-style *Taiji Quan* in which the fist techniques are used. In this exercise, the fist is forced down from above with a forward step as if planting a tree.

Methods of Practice

Move the right foot forward, heel first on the ground, and turn the body slightly to the right. At the same time, draw the right palm back in a curved shape to the front of the right waist, and move the left palm from below in a curved shape to block to the forward left. Eyes look ahead (Fig. 7-101).

Keep the right tiptoes outward and firm on the ground, and shift the body weight to the right leg. Raise the left foot and step forward, heel first on the ground, and gradually shift the body weight forward. Keep the left foot firm on the ground, and straighten the right leg to form the Left Bow Step. At the same time, move the left palm in a curved shape and grab and press it to the lower left, palm facing down and fingers forward, and press it by the left hip. Clench the right palm into fist and strike down forward. Eyes look at the striking point (Figs. 7-102 A, B).

Inhale when landing the right step, drawing back the fist and blocking, and exhale when striking down. In the mind, the fist hits to the infinite depth.

Essential Points

(1) When drawing the right fist back to the waist, do not move it too far backward. Keep the elbow naturally bent and the left thumb apart. Do not lean the body backward.

171

(b) Strike Palm Forward Step

This is the ... method ... in which the beginner is required to do the exercise from ... foot down ... step in ... parallel circles.

Method of this:

Move ... and ... forward ... and forward ... foot slightly to ... then the ... forward ... the ... down ... and the ... circle ... the ... (Fig. 7-101)

Fig. 7-101

Fig. 7-102A   Fig. 7-102B

172

(2) When striking down with the fist, turn the body slightly to the left so that the front side faces forward, and keep the left palm and right fist almost at the same height.

(3) Keep the left arm bent inward, the right arm straight but slightly bent, and the right fist due forward in front of the body, not inclined to the right.

(4) When striking with the fist, do not lean the upper part of the body too much.

(5) Grabbing with the palm, striking with the fist and shifting the body weight must be well-coordinated. In the fixed form, the fist and the palm are integrated.

Striking down with the fist is a method of hitting the lower part of the enemy's body. It can also be used to prevent the enemy from attacking with his legs.

(38) Grasp Peacock's Tail with Forward Step

Methods of Practice

Shift the body weight slightly backward, raise the left tiptoes, keeping them inward, and then shift the body

Fig. 7-103

weight forward to the left leg. Move the right foot a half step forward, tiptoes on the ground. At the same time, turn the body slightly to the right, raise the left palm in a curved shape to the upper left, and change the right fist into palm, palm facing up, moving it to the left (Fig. 7-103).

Raise the right foot and move it one step forward, heel first on the ground. Then gradually shift the body weight forward and keep the right foot firm on the ground. At the same time, move the right arm forward for an upward parry. Place the left palm under the right arm. The following movements are the same as described in the exercises for Grasp Peacock's Tail (Figs. 7-104–107).

(39) Single Whip

The same as described in the previous exercises from Grasp Peacock's Tail to Single Whip (Figs. 7-108–109).

(40) Push Down

Methods of Practice

Shift the body weight backward, bend the right leg and squat to form the crouch stance. At the same time, withdraw and move the left palm in a curved shape backward, inward and downward, and thrust it forward from the chest through the inner side of the left leg, palm facing right. Eyes on the left palm (Fig. 7-110).

The essential points are the same as described in the previous exercise Push Down.

(41) Step Forward to Form Seven Stars

Place the crossed fists in front of the chest to protect the middle (the chest or central Dantian), similar to the Plough in the evening sky.

Fig. 7-104

Fig. 7-105

Fig. 7-106

Fig. 7-107

Fig. 7-108   Fig. 7-109

Fig. 7-110

176

Methods of Practice

Shift the body weight forward to the left leg. While thrusting the left palm forward, open the right hook gradually into palm, and thrust it forward from behind in a curved shape together with the shifting of the body forward. When moving the hands forward and past the body, change both palms into fists, cross the hands, raise them and place them in front of the chest. At the same time, raise the right foot from behind, move it past the left foot and step forward, tiptoes on the ground to form the Right Empty Step. Eyes look straight ahead (Figs. 7-111–112).

Essential Points

(1) As the right hand moves along a long line, the speed of the right hand should be a bit quicker than the left hand.

(2) When thrusting the palms, the left hand is in front, and the right hand in rear. The movement of both hands should be completed at the same time when changed into

Fig. 7-111   Fig. 7-112

fists.

(3) The movements of the hands and feet should be coordinated. When the movements of the crossed hands are completed, the formation of the Right Empty Step should also be completed.

(4) When crossing the hands, extend both arms fully into a round circle, not too close to the body.

(5) Keep balance, head slightly up. Do not shrug the shoulders.

This exercise is effective for defence. Use both fists to ward off the enemy's attack. The right foot can be raised at any time to attack the lower part of the enemy's body.

(42) Mount Tiger with Backward Step

Block with the upper hand and press with the lower hand. Mount Tiger provides an imposing posture for the practitioner if he does it well.

Methods of Practice

Move the right leg one step backward and shift the body weight backward, tiptoes on the ground. At the same time, change both fists into palms, move them downward in a curved shape, and then move them apart, the right palm should be raised above the upper right of the head, palm facing outside, and left palm pressed to near the outer side of the left hip, palm facing down and fingers forward. Eyes look ahead (Fig. 7-113).

Breathe naturally throughout the exercise. Be calm, and keep the mind on Dantian.

Essential Points

(1) Embrace while opening the arms. Keep the chest in, relax the back and waist, and sit on the hips.

(2) The hands are pitted against each other at a distance.

In combat, Mount Tiger with Backward Step involves

Fig. 7-113

the backward step for dodging to parry and block the enemy's attack, and the empty step to advance and to look for an opportunity to attack.

(43) Lotus Kick with Body Turn

In this exercise, both the hands and feet are used together for attack. Move the feet and twist the body, with a large range of change in the space. Keep balance.

Methods of Practice

Move the left foot to the right side, heel first on the ground, and turned inward. At the same time, turn the body to the right, move the left arm to the right in a curved shape to encircle the left chest, and move the right palm from above to the right downward and then encircle to the left. Eyes look backward to the right (Fig. 7-114).

Keep the left foot inward and firmly on the ground, continuing to turn the body to the right. Turn both feet naturally together with the turn of the body, right heel

179

slightly off the ground, and shift the body weight to the left leg. At the same time, swing the palms in curved shape to the right, right palm placed to the forward right and left palm placed inside the right elbow, and both palms facing outside. Eyes look forward to the right (Fig. 7-115).

Use the waist to turn the body slightly to the left. Bend the right leg and raise it, and swing the right foot from below in a curved shape to the upper left and then to the upper right. At the same time, pat the instep with both palms from left and from right. Turn the body to the right at the same time (Fig. 7-116).

Breathe naturally throughout the exercise. In the mind, the hands and feet are integrated.

Essential Points

(1) In turning the body and feet, the movements should be quick and relaxed.

(2) In the process of executing the lotus kick, use the waist to turn the body and guide the leg movements.

In combat, this exercise is a method of attacking the enemy with kicks, and the part to be attacked is the face.

(44) Bend Bow to Shoot Tiger

Pull the two fists apart as if drawing a bow.

Methods of Practice

Move the right foot backward to the right, turn the body to the right and shift the body weight to the right. Change the palms into fists and swing them in a curved shape from upper left downward and to the right. Eyes follow the fists (Figs. 7-117 A, B).

Continue to shift the body weight to the right to form the Right Bow Step. Put up a right fist block on the upper right of the head, fist centre facing outside, and punch outward with the left fist from the chest, fist eye up. Eyes look at the punch point (Fig. 7-118).

Fig. 7-114

Fig. 7-115

Fig. 7-116

181

Fig. 7-117A

Fig. 7-117B

Fig. 7-118

Inhale when swinging the fists, and exhale when punching and blocking. In the mind, the fist is extended to an infinite distance.

Essential Points

(1) Turn the body to the right when swinging the fists, and turn the body slightly to the left when punching.

(2) Keep both arms bent and the waist erect.

The exercise uses the right fist to block the attacking fist from the opponent, and the left fist to hit the opponent's chest and ribs.

(45) Parry and Punch

Methods of Practice

Shift the body weight to the left, left tiptoes outward, turn the body to the left, and withdraw the right foot, tiptoes on the ground. Pull the right fist from above downward in a curved shape to the front of the chest, change the left fist into palm. Turn the left arm inward and lower it, palm facing up and opposite to the right fist

Fig. 7-119

(Fig. 7-119).

The following movements and essential points are the same as described for the previous exercise Parry and Punch (Figs. 7-120–123).

(46) Apparent Close Up

The movements and essential points in this exercise are the same as described in Exercise 10 for Apparent Close Up (Fig. 7-124).

(47) Crossed Hands

Methods of Practice

Turn the body to the right, left tiptoes raised and inward. Bend the right leg to form a Side Bow, straighten the left leg, and shift the body weight to the right leg. At the same time, move the right palm from left to right in a curved shape. Eyes on the right palm (Fig. 7-125).

The following movements are the same as described for the previous exercise Crossed Hands (Fig. 7-126).

(48) Finishing Form

Methods of Practice

Extend the palms horizontally forward, palms facing up. Keep the arms apart, slightly wider than the shoulders. Eyes look ahead (Fig. 7-127).

Turn the arms inward and turn the palms over to face down. Lower the shoulders, drop the elbows and press the palms downward. Eyes look down (Fig. 7-128).

Keep both hands by the sides of the body, draw the left foot back to the right foot, and stand still with hands down. Eyes look ahead (Fig. 7-129).

Breathe naturally throughout the exercise.

Keep calm and serene, hold the energy together and

Fig. 7-120

Fig. 7-121

Fig. 7-122

Fig. 7-123

Fig. 7-124

Fig. 7-125

Fig. 7-126

Fig. 7-127

Fig. 7-128

Fig. 7-129

return it to the original.

Essential Points

Keep the head upright and the body erect. Relax the waist and hips.

Appendix: Questions and Answers

1. I have learned another style of *Taiji Quan*. Can I learn the Yang-style *Taiji Quan* now? Can I learn different styles of *Taiji Quan* at the same time? Do they affect each other?

Answer: If you have learned another style of *Taiji Quan*, you can also learn the Yang-style and even faster. The differences among the different schools of *Taiji Quan* lie in style, range of movement, rhythm treatment and direction, but their basic theory is the same. The general characteristic of movement—curved movement is also the same. The combinations of hand and foot movements are also similar to each other. Learning different schools of boxing for comparison can be helpful to improvement. The origin of the different schools of *Taiji Quan* is also believed to be the same. Moreover, many famous *Taiji Quan* masters in the past also practised more than one school or style. However, attention should be paid to the following points:

(1) Concentrate on one style of *Taiji Quan* at the beginning instead of several different styles at the same time. If you learn different styles at the same time at the start, you might possibly mix them together with the result that there are no differences among the different styles. Learn a new style only after you have grasped all the basic skills of one style and the technique of the complete style.

(2) Practise the basic movements thoroughly. The basic movements embody the rhythms of the inherent movement of all schools of *Taiji Quan*. Practice makes perfect.

(3) If you have learned several schools of *Taiji Quan*,

you should stop for a while after you practice one style before practising another.

2. When is the best time for practising *Taiji Quan*?

Answer: *Taiji Quan* can be practised at any time and at any place. Generally speaking, in the morning before breakfast is the best time. It can help to promote blood circulation of the whole body, keep your brain fresh, make you very energetic, and increase your appetite. Moreover, after some hours of mental work, to practise *Taiji Quan* helps to fully regulate the nervous system, relax the body and mind, and replenish the energy needed by the cerebrum. Thirdly, two hours after supper is also good for *Taiji Quan*. In short, it depends on how you make your own arrangements in connection with your work and life. Practise when you are free. However, you are advised not to practise *Taiji Quan* shortly after you have a meal, or when you are completely exhausted after long hours of physical work, or when you are in low spirits.

3. Are there any taboos for practising *Taiji Quan*? What are the points for attention for people with poor health?

Answer: There are no taboos for practising *Taiji Quan*. The movements in the Yang-style are soft. They have no negative effects on the body and are therefore good for all types of people. When people with poor health or illness practise *Taiji Quan*, they should properly control the amount of exercise so that they do not feel tired. If they sweat a little, that means the result are good. However, care should be taken not to catch cold. These people should not extend their range of movement too much. They should concentrate on combining their minds and movements into one so as to achieve a better internal exercise.

4. Some people do *Taiji Quan* exercises using music. Is

this good for practice?

Answer: It is in the last few decades that people have been doing *Taiji Quan* exercises accompanied by music. It is now popular in many parts of China, especially when people practice *Taiji Quan* in groups. Listening to music is an important way to regulate the body and mind. This is the same with *Taiji Quan*. Therefore, if appropriate music is used, it adds good atmosphere and acts as a guide in the exercises. Especially for beginners, it helps to calm their minds. However, attention should be paid to the following points: (1) The music should be soft, slow and smooth. Music with strong rhythms should not be used; (2) Music serves only as a foil. The movements should not be executed entirely according to the melodic variations in order to avoid changes in the speed of movements; (3) It is advisable not to use music when you have learned *Taiji Quan* to a certain degree.

5. Are there any requirements for clothing and foot-wear in practising *Taiji Quan*?

Answer: The heels of the shoes used should not be too high. Shoes without heels and made with soft materials are the best choice, such as Chinese shoes made with cloth. Put on more clothes in winter if you do the exercises outdoors to avoid stiff muscles and wrong movements.

6. Body weight shifts from time to time in doing the *Taiji Quan* exercises. What are the points for attention in this situation?

Answer: The shift of body weight when doing *Taiji Quan* exercises is an important part of the interchange between yin and yang. It must conform to the rule of the yin and yang philosophy. First of all, the shift should be round and natural, with no sudden changes. All transitions between the two movements should be natural. Secondly, it is essential to prioritize the feet—the key part of the body. Whether in advancing, retreating, or stepping to any side, move the feet first, and then the ankle, hips, waist and body, one by one. This helps to consolidate the exercises and to ensure that every part of the body moves. Thirdly, it is important to handle well the proportion of burden experienced by both legs. The weight on the legs is equally divided in the balance step. The weight is on the supporting leg in the one-leg step. In all other steps, the body weight is evenly divided by both the legs. In the fixed form, if all the movements are executed precisely, and you feel natural and comfortable, it means the proportions are correct. It is difficult to tell the precise amount of weight in a simple way, because the physique and body weight of each individual are different. It requires repeated practice.

7. What is the best way to breathe in Yang-style *Taiji Quan*?

Answer: There are several levels of breathing in the Yang-style. At the beginning, stress should be laid on the movements; that is, breathing with the execution of the opening, closing, extending and flexing movements. After some time, you will be able to use the movements to guide the breathing or to automatically make changes in breathing in the process of executing movements. At a still higher stage, you can use "natural breathing" freely: that is, control breathing entirely according to the needs of the internal organs. Of the above-described levels, the "movement-guided breathing" is the most important, and particular attention should be paid to it. The beginners should take the following advice:

(1) Do not hold your breath at any time. The movements of *Taiji Quan* are always flowing, smooth and varied, and there should be no pauses in breathing or there will be no harmony between the movements and breathing; (2) The frequency and depth of breathing depend on

each exercise. If the exercise takes a long time, the breathing can be milder and longer. If the exercise takes a short time, the breathing can be deeper. In either case, however, it must be even and slow; (3) Grasp the general rules for breathing: inhale when the exercise starts, and exhale when the exercise finishes. The nose is used to inhale, and the mouth to exhale. However, there are exceptions.

8. What are the books recommended for studying the theory of the Yang-style *Taiji Quan*?

Answer: If you have time to read some articles and books on *Taiji Quan*, it would be good for practising the sport. I would like to recommend two classical books: (1) *On Taiji Quan* by Wang Zongyue is the most well-known work in the history of *Taiji Quan*. It was the first to make a systematic interpretation of the theory and principles concerning *Taiji*. It deals in detail with how the *Taiji* theory was applied to *Taiji Quan*, and describes the essential points and rules for the practice of *Taiji Quan*. All *Taiji Quan* masters since Wang's time have spoken highly of this work; (2) *Complete Work on Yang-Style Taiji Quan* by Yang Chengfu describes how the exercises in the Yang-style are done and analyzes its push-hand technique. It includes many articles on *Taiji Quan*, as well as pictures showing Yang Chengfu at play in the boxing movements.

9. How does one correctly understand the words "relax" and "soft" in the Yang-style *Taiji Quan*, and how does one do them well?

Answer: "Relax" and "soft" are the requirements for all the exercises in the Yang-style *Taiji Quan*, not merely one particular exercise, movement or posture. The essence of "relax" and "soft" is to free the body and mind from tension so that the functions of the human body can be brought into full play. When practising the Yang-style *Taiji Quan*, you must have a natural and calm mind, which is the basic guarantee for "relax" and "soft." Moreover, the movements must be stable and steady, the play must be light, and the joints for all movements must be supple. Breathing must be dropped down instead of held in the chest. The limbs must be fully stretched, and the spinal column upright. When practising "relaxed" and "soft" movements, avoid the common mistake of "looseness"—all limbs weak and powerless, with the waist and body restrained. This is the result of misunderstanding the words "relax" and "soft."

10. How do you practise the *Taiji* push-hand after practising *Taiji Quan*?

Answer: The *Taiji* push-hand is an important part of the *Taiji Quan* system. It is also a valuable supplement to the practice of *Taiji Quan*. Some of the powers and methods used in *Taiji Quan* can be verified in the push-hand. If there are two or more people able to practise together, they can start the push-hand practice on the basis of grasping the eight basic methods of *Taiji Quan*. The way to practise the push-hand is first to do the single movement exercise—the upward parry, for example—and then combine the movement with the power and stance. If a *Taiji Quan* teacher is available to give guidance and proceed, step by step, the effect will be better.

图书在版编目 (CIP) 数据

太极拳——杨式：英文/余功保著；李士伋绘图 . —北京：
外文出版社，1996
（中国武术丛书）

ISBN 7 - 119 - 01807 - 8

Ⅰ. 太… Ⅱ. ①余… ②李… Ⅲ. 太极拳，杨式 – 中国 – 英文
Ⅳ. G852.11

中国版本图书馆 CIP 数据核字 (95) 第 23584 号

太极拳——杨式

余功保　　著

李士伋　绘图

*

Ⓒ外文出版社

外文出版社出版

（中国北京百万庄大街 24 号）

邮政编码 100037

北京外文印刷厂印刷

中国国际图书贸易总公司发行

（中国北京车公庄西路 35 号）

北京邮政信箱第 399 号　邮政编码 100044

1996 年（大 32 开）第 1 版

1998 年第 1 版第 2 次印刷

（英）

ISBN 7 - 119 - 01807 - 8/G·91（外）

01550

7 - E - 3072P